C000002120

AVIATION MUSEUMS
OF BRITAIN

Ken Ellis

Midland Publishing Limited

Copyright © 1998 Ken Ellis

This second edition published by
Midland Publishing Limited
24 The Hollow, Earl Shilton
Leicester, LE9 7NA, England

ISBN 1 85780 078 8

Design concept and layout
© Midland Publishing Limited and
Stephen Thompson Associates

Printed by
WBC Book Manufacturers Ltd
Bridgend, Mid Glamorgan

Title Page Illustration:
'Guarding' the main entrance to the
Museum of Army Flying at Middle Wallop,
Hampshire, is DHC Beaver AL.1 XP822.
(Ian Howell)

Cover Illustrations courtesy:
Front, Ken Ellis; Rear, both Roger Richards.

CONTENTS

Acknowledgements
Many thanks go to all of the curators, information
officers, volunteers etc who responded to the
questionnaire that was sent out fact finding for
this book. Thanks also to the museums who
helped with illustrations. Other photographs came
from many friends around the country and they
are credited with their work. Continued thanks
goes to the small army of loyal scribes who
contribute regularly to *Wrecks & Relics* – they get
mentioned in despatches in Edition 16! To Pete
West, Russell Strong and the team at Midland
and of course to Pam and Fleas.

INTRODUCTION

The first edition of *AMB* was well greeted by readers and museums alike and this second edition aims to continue to provide a wide range range of information on the ever-increasing number of aviation museums and related venues in the British Isles.

Acknowledging that many an aviation enthusiast is to be found happy as a lamb wending through the locomotives at a steam museum, or vintage car collection or the Victoria & Albert, this book aims to provide a wider view of what is available. For many, there is also the family to take into consideration and a visit to an aviation museum can be extended to find something else that will please the rest of the household as well. This book has been devised to offer other alternatives, hopefully not by way of a sop to 'her indoors' but to allow *everyone* to find venues of interest and, who knows, to make it easier to visit an aviation museum next time!

With the co-operation of the museums concerned, greatly expanded information has been given on the facilities that are available at museums – some that may be quite crucial to a successful family day out. It is believed that *AMB* is the first aviation museum guide ever to provide details of how to travel to these venues by public transport and which offer help to the disabled.

Great emphasis has been made of the excellent services to be had from the Tourist Boards, a source all too frequently overlooked by many visitors. The book has adopted, with a few 'tweaks' the larger 'regions' used by the English Tourist Boards as a more useful way of showing touring possibilities.

Another cornerstone of the book has been to cover *only* museums and collections that are *truly* open to the public on a regular basis. The general ruling has been only to include venues that are at least open at weekends throughout the summer season. Other venues that genuinely encourage visitors by prior arrangement are given briefer mentions. In this edition, other venue suggestions include an increasing number of locations that display airframes, but cannot be called museums – for example shopping centres!

The illustrations attempt to show the broad sweep of aviation museums in Britain – there is a wondrous variety out there to sample. Hence there are photographs of displays, as well as airframes for it is often the latter that 'capture' visitors for longer. To add further flavour to the pictorial element some views of exhibits 'in action' before retirement are also included.

The contents of *AMB* reflects input from readers who clearly are looking for much more than a 'field with aircraft in' when travelling the country. Comments, suggestions and additions are very welcome so that the next edition will 'work' even harder for you!

Ken Ellis
Barrowden, Rutland
June 1998

HOW TO USE THIS GUIDE

The guide is arranged by large regional area, essentially corresponding to those adopted by the Tourist Boards. Each region heading includes the counties grouped in that area and telephone and fax number of the Regional Tourist Board(s) (RTB) responsible for the area. General tourist enquires can be handled by the Tourist Information Centre (TIC) number given in the specific museum reference, but more regional enquiries may well be best centred on the RTB.

Museum Information

The following information is given :

Name – Name of the museum in question.
Location – Nearest town/village and county.
Address – Postal address.
Where – Directions by car.
Telephone – Telephone (and fax, e-mail and web-site if applicable) number of the museum. The telephone number will usually be office hours only. If available at other times, this will be stated.
Open – Opening times and days correct at the time of going to press.
By bus – Details of local bus services that go to, or near the museum. More details from the TIC – see below.
By rail – Nearest railway (or tube) station with as-the-crow-flies distance to the museum.
Tourist – Telephone (and fax if applicable) of the local Tourist Information Centre to which general enquires can be made. TIC's can provide a vast range of information, including details of places to visit within a 50 miles radius; accommodation; restaurants, cafes etc; travel information etc. In general, they are open Monday to Friday 9am to 5pm, with longer hours, including weekend opening, during the summer months. A TIC marked * is not open all year. In that case, the nearest all-year alternative is given.

Admission – Admission prices correct at the time of going to press. Discounts for larger parties may also apply, please check with the museum.

Facilities – It would be an impossible task to list every facility available. Some of the more practical ones have been itemised. As before, make enquiries with the museum involved before setting out if you are unsure of anything.

Toilets	Toilets/washroom facilities on site.
Parking	Own car park.
Cafe	Catering facilities on site. These may range from a drinks/food vending machines to cafe facilities to restaurant, or combinations of such facilities. Use the museum 'phone number to check if unsure.
Shop	Gift shop or similar on site. Again, this may vary in size and in the range of items stocked.
Disabled	Facilities for the disabled. If in doubt, enquire of the museum on the telephone number given.
Kids	Children's play area or similar.
All	Considered to be a genuine 'all-weather' venue, ie the museum offers extensive areas undercover and that a visit in poor weather would not totally ruin the trip.
Changes	Displays regularly changed so that a visit a year later would provide something different to see.
Brochure	Sending a large stamped addressed envelope to the museum address given will bring an information leaflet by return.
X	Museum did not reply to the questionnaire sent to them during the compiling of this edition.
*	Any of the above codes shown with an asterisk (eg Disabled*) signifies a partial facility, eg disabled access not possible to all areas.

Note: *All facilities are listed in good faith using the most up-to-date information available to the compiler. Visitors are urged to telephone ahead with specific enquires to avoid disappointment.*

Museum Narrative

A brief description of the museum is given in narrative form. This includes a general description of the collecting policy of the museum, special features and items of interest. Readers are reminded that displays, special features and aircraft exhibits may change at quite short notice. To avoid disappointment, contact the museum in question before setting out.

Aircraft Exhibit Tables

Column 1 – Aircraft are listed in alpha-numeric order, with civilian aircraft first, then military, then aircraft that carry no form of identification marking. A number in quotation marks indicates that it carries spurious markings.

Column 2 – Manufacturer, name, designation and marque number. With rarer types, some further explanation (eg homebuilt, man-powered aircraft, reproduction etc) is given, where space permits. Incomplete aircraft (cockpit sections, nose sections, fuselage etc) are also denoted here. Full-scale models (representing a type in size and shape but not true construction technique) are shown as – FSM. *Original* design houses are used for the naming of each type. (An exception to this has been Westland's production of the Dragonfly/Widgeon, Whirlwind and Wessex under licence from Sikorsky – as these types have been extensively developed beyond the original design house.)

It has been necessary to abbreviate some manufacturers names, as follows:

ANEC	Air Navigation & Engineering Co
BA	British Klemm Aeroplane Co
BAC	British Aircraft Corporation
BP	Boulton Paul
Con	Consolidated Aircraft
CASA	Construcciones Aeronauticas SA
DH	de Havilland
DHA	de Havilland Australia
DHC	de Havilland Canada
EE	English Electric
FMA	Fábrica Militar de Aviones
GD	General Dynamics
HP	Handley Page
HS	Hawker Siddeley
LVG	Luft Verkehrs Gesellschaft
MBB	Messerschmitt-Bölkow-Blohm
MiG	Mikoyan-Gurevich
MS	Morane Saulnier (also SOCATA)
McDD	McDonnell Douglas
NA	North American
RAF	Royal Aircraft Factory
SAAB	Svenska Aeroplan AB
SAL	Scottish Aviation Ltd
SNIAS	Société Nationale Industrielle Aérospatiale
Sup	Supermarine
V-S	Vickers-Supermarine

The evolution of names for manufacturers during the production life of an aircraft type can be a minefield for compilers of works such as this guide. Some latitude has been given which may upset purists. For example, the Buccaneer S.1 has been attributed to Blackburn, but the S.2 to Hawker Siddeley. The main aim has been to avoid such horrors as 'BAe Spitfire' which have crept into other reference works!

Beyond this appears information in brackets that may help the visitor to further identify an exhibit. Items in *rounded* brackets may give a real identity (if a spurious one is given in Column 1) or other form of identity not worn on the airframe. A common example of the latter is a British Aviation Preservation Council (BAPC) identity number, applied to aircraft that lack any other form of identity. Items in *squared* brackets relate to prominent code markings worn on aircraft, eg [8-NY] or [NN-D].

The symbol ✈ is used to denote an aircraft airworthy at time of going to press.

Column 3 – Gives country of origin and year of manufacture. Country of origin is that of the *original* design house. The following abbreviations apply :

Arg	Argentina
Aus	Austria
Aust	Australia
Bel	Belgium
Can	Canada
Cz	Czechoslovakia
Fr	France
Gr	Germany
It	Italy
Ja	Japan
Neth	Netherlands
Pol	Poland
Ru	Russia, ie the former USSR
Sp	Spain
Swn	Sweden
Sws	Switzerland
US	United States of America

As the vast majority of aircraft exhibits in British museums are of British origin, if a country of origin code is not given, then it is British. Where a year of manufacture is prefixed with a 'c' (eg c75) this denotes an approximation. To save space, years have had the '19' removed, except for 19th century dates. With reproductions (or 'replicas'), the year of manufacture is given for the *original* type upon which it was based – as this gives a better indication of the era the museum is striving to illustrate.

Prefixing this information may be the symbol § which indicates that at the time of going to press the aircraft was stored (perhaps not even on site) or otherwise, and not available for public inspection. For major collections (eg the Fleet Air Arm Museum, RAF Museum) with extensive off-site storage facilities, no attempt has been made to list stored airframes.

Also:
Details of other events staged at the venue and items of interest etc staged in the immediate vicinity. (If applicable)

Nearby:
Details of other museums, interesting venues etc within a 20 mile radius of the museum in question. A particular leaning towards transport and industrial museums etc has been adopted. This section is designed to provide hints to help plan a full day (or weekend, or holiday) within the area – greater details from the TICs. Venues listed are not intended to be comprehensive and inevitably reflect the whims of the compiler. Distances given are as-the-crow-flies. Comments from readers as to other venues to be included in the next edition are very welcome.

Also in:
Where applicable, details are given of other aviation items of interest within the region. These will include collections that are not open to the general public on a regular basis and that require prior permission, but happily entertain visitors on this basis.

Important
The information contained in this guide is given in good faith on the basis of information submitted to, and research by, the compiler. Every effort has been made to be as accurate as possible. However, neither the compiler nor the Publishers can be held responsible for any errors, misinterpretations or omissions that may occur. All liability for loss, disappointment, negligence or other damage caused by reliance on the information contained in this guide is hereby excluded.

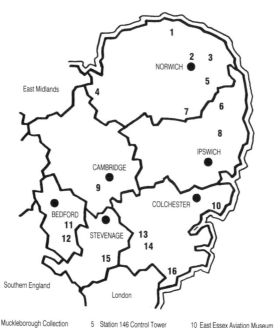

EAST ANGLIA
Bedfordshire, Cambridgeshire, Essex, Hertfordshire, Norfolk, Suffolk

1 Muckleborough Collection
2 City of Norwich Aviation Museum
3 Ludham Control Tower and Military Museum
4 Fenland West Norfolk Aviation Museum
5 Station 146 Control Tower Museum, Seething
6 Norfolk & Suffolk Aviation Museum
7 100th BG Memorial Museum
8 390th BG Memorial Museum
9 Imperial War Museum, Duxford
10 East Essex Aviation Museum
11 Shuttleworth Collection
12 Stondon Transport Museum
13 North Weald Airfield Museum
14 Blake Hall
15 Mosquito Aircraft Museum
16 Thameside Aviation Museum

East Anglia Tourist Board
Toppesfield Hall, Hadleigh, Suffolk, IP7 5DN
Tel: 01473 822922 Fax: 01473 823063

BLAKE HALL 'OPS' ROOM AND AIRSCENE MUSEUM
Chipping Ongar, Essex

Address: Blake Hall, Bovinger, nr Ongar, Essex.
Telephone: 01277 363328.
Where: Near Bovinger, N of the A414 Harlow to Chipping Ongar Road. Junction 7 off the M11.
Open: Daily 11am to 5pm, Easter to October.
By bus: Buses serve North Weald Bassett and Chipping Ongar.
By rail: Epping Underground, Central Line, 5 mls
Tourist: Chelmsford 01245 283400, Fax: 01245 354026. Saffron Walden 01799 510444.
Admission: Adult £1.50, Child 50p.
Facilities: Toilets/Parking/Shop/Kids/All/ Changes/Brochure/X.

Within this fine 17th century house, which also has famous gardens open to the public, was located the operations room for the RAF's 'Sector E' after it was bombed at the nearby North Weald airfield. The 'ops' room with its status boards, plotter charts, viewing balcony etc have all been lovingly restored since 1984 to produce a unique museum. The Airscene Museum extends the story still further with a wealth of display material. Guided tours provide for a very personal visit.

Nearby:
Central London, 20 miles.
North Weald Airfield Heritage Museum, 3 miles, page 18.
Hatfield House, 18 miles
Mosquito Aircraft Museum, 20 miles.
Museum of Artillery, 18 miles, page 39.
RAF Museum, 20 miles, page 40.
Thameside Aviation Museum, 20 miles, page 24.

EAST ESSEX AVIATION MUSEUM AND MUSEUM OF THE 1940s near St Osyth, Essex

Address: Albert E Scott, 1 Kestrel Way, Clacton-on-Sea, Essex, CO15 4JD..
Where: Within the Point Clear Caravan Park at the end of an unclassified road from St Osyth, west of Clacton-on-Sea.
Open: Throughout the year: Sun 10am to 2pm; Mon 7pm to 10pm. Additionally, June to September Wed and Thur 10am to 2pm; Sun and Bank Hols 10am to 4pm. Other times by appointment.
By bus: Bus service from Clacton to the Caravan Park.
By rail: Clacton, 5 miles.
Tourist: Clacton 01255 423400.
Admission: Free – donations welcomed.
Facilities: Toilets*/Parking/Cafe*/Shop/Kids*/ All/Changes/Brochure. * These facilities a few yards away. Because of the nature of the building, disabled access only to ground floor.

Located within a coastline look-out Martello tower, the museum includes a wealth of material on wartime aerial activity in the area, items recovered from the sea and local crash sites. Dominating this is the very complete wreckage of Mustang *Little Zippie* that crashed off-shore in January 1945. There are also displays showing life in wartime Essex. On a clear day, the view from the top of the tower is incredible!

Aircraft exhibit:

☐ 44-14574	NA P-51D Mustang wreck	US '44

Nearby:
Clacton-on-Sea, 5 miles.
Clacton Aerodrome, (pleasure flying, viewing area) 5 miles.
Maritime Museum, Harwich 16 miles.

FENLAND & WEST NORFOLK AVIATION MUSEUM
near Wisbech, Cambridgeshire

Address: Peter Winning, *Farndale House*, Outwell Road, Emneth, Wisbech, PE14 0DU.
Where: Located at Bamber's Garden Centre, Old Lynn Road, West Walton Highway, near Wisbech – off the A47/B198 junction and signposted from the A47.
Open: Weekends and Bank Holidays, April to September 9.30am to 5pm. Weekends March and October 10am to 4pm.
By bus: Peterborough to King's Lynn service passes the museum gates.
By rail: King's Lynn, 10 miles.
Tourist: Wisbech 01945 583263, Fax: 01945 582784.
Admission: Adult £1.50, child/cons 75p.
Facilities: Toilets/Parking/Cafe/Shop/Disabled/ Kids/All/Changes/Brochure.

Run by the Fenland & West Norfolk Aircraft Preservation Society, the museum is centred around a small collection of aircraft and an astounding collection of aircraft engines and exhibits illustrating the history of military aviation in the Fens and Norfolk. The museum is well known for its restoration to pristine condition of aero engines salvaged from crash sites and has won a major award for the restoration of a Vampire. Among new exhibits is a Boeing 747 simulator and the cockpit section of one of the MiG-29 *Fulcrum*. The garden centre's facilities are available to museum visitors, including a tea room and an aquatic centre.

Aircraft exhibits:

☐ G-ARNH	Piper Colt 108		§ US '61
☐ XD434	DH Vampire T.11 [25]		'54
☐ XM402	Hunting Jet Provost T.3 [J]		'58
☐ XP488	Slingsby Grasshopper TX.1		§ '62
☐ XS420	EE Lightning T.5		'65
☐ XS459	EE Lightning T.5 [AW]		'65

Nearby:
King's Lynn, *12 miles*.
Long Sutton Butterfly and Falconry Park, *8 miles*.
Sandringham, *16 miles*.
Wildfowl Trust, *Peakirk 20 miles*.

Part of the main display hall at the Fenland & West Norfolk Aviation Museum. Scope and depth is excellent – engines a speciality! Ken Ellis

IMPERIAL WAR MUSEUM

Duxford, Cambridgeshire

Address: Duxford Airfield, Duxford, CB2 4QR.

Telephone: 01223 835000, Events Hotline 0891 516816, Fax: 01223 837267. Web-site: http://www.iwm.org.uk Pleasure flying enquiries on 0870 902 6146.

Open: Daily 10am to 6pm mid-March to late October and 10am to 4pm the remainder of the year. Last admission 45 mins before closing. Closed New Year's Day and Dec 24-26.

By bus: On various bus routes, details from TIC.

By rail: Whittlesford 3 miles.

Tourist: Cambridge 01223 322640, Fax: 01223 463385.

Admission: Adult £7, OAP £4.70, child/cons £3.50, Family ticket £20. Charges differ for special event days. Special rates for parties of 20 or more.

Facilities: Toilets/Parking/Cafe/Shop/Disabled/ Kids/All/Changes/Brochure.

Run in conjunction with the Duxford Aviation Society (DAS) and Cambridgeshire County Council, Duxford is a huge and vibrant centre which benefits from being on a 'live' airfield. The Imperial War Museum (IWM – see also South Lambeth, London) has the majority of its aircraft collection at Duxford, and offers views of aircraft under restoration. In August 1997 the incredible American Air Museum was opened, devoted to the history of US air power. Not just aircraft, the impressive Land Warfare Exhibition Hall (with connecting light railway) contains a large array of vehicles in battlefield scenes. Frequent special exhibitions are staged and Duxford is often used for rallies, fly-ins etc. Duxford was a former fighter base and the Operations Room has been restored to its Battle of Britain guise. Simulator rides* and pleasure flying* also available. There are several airshows* during the year, crowned by the Flying Legends display each July. Most days two of the DAS collection of civil airliners, normally including Concorde, are available for public inspection. Duxford is home to a wide range of classic aircraft and 'warbird' operators and their aircraft can frequently be seen flying or under maintenance, during a visit or airshow. Resident operators include: the Aircraft Restoration Company, B-17 Preservation Ltd, Classic Wings, The Fighter Collection, Old Flying Machine Company and Plane Sailing Ltd.

* Extra charges apply.

Aircraft exhibits:

☐ G-AFBS	Miles Magister I	'39
☐ G-AGJG	DH Dragon Rapide	§ '41
☐ G-AGTO	Auster J/1 Autocrat →	'45
☐ G-AIYR	DH Dragon Rapide →	'44
☐ G-AKAZ	Piper L-4A Grasshopper → [HL-6¾] US '42	
☐ G-ALDG	HP Hermes 4 fuselage	'49
☐ G-ALFU	DH Dove 6	'48
☐ G-ALWF	Vickers Viscount 701	'52
☐ G-ALZO	Airspeed Ambassador	'50
☐ G-ANTK	Avro York	'46
☐ G-AOVT	Bristol Britannia 312	'58
☐ G-APDB	DH Comet 4	'58
☐ G-APWJ	HP Herald 201	'59
☐ G-ASGC	Vickers Super VC-10	'63

☐ G-AVFB	HS Trident 2E	'68
☐ G-AVMU	BAC 111-510ED	'69
☐ G-AWAH	Beech Baron D55 →	'68
☐ G-AXDN	BAC/SNIAS Concorde 101	UK/Fr '71
☐ G-AZSC	NA Harvard IIB → [43-SC]	US '43
☐ G-BSBT	Piper J-3C-65 Cub →	US c38
☐ G-BWFM	Yakovlev Yak-50 →	Ru c77
☐ G-IVAR	Yakovlev Yak-50 →	Ru c77
☐ G-OPAS	Vickers Viscount 806 nose	'58
☐ G-USUK	Colt 2500A balloon gondola	'87
☐ N4845V	Grumman FM-2 Wildcat → [F]	US '42
☐ VR-BPS	Con PBY-5A Catalina → [P]	US '44
☐ 'D8084'	Bristol F.2b Fighter (G-ACAA)	'18
☐ E2581	Bristol F.2b Fighter	'18
☐ F3556	RAF RE.8	'18

☐ 'L8841'	Bristol Bolingbroke IVT →	
	(G-BPIV) [QY-C]	
		'42
☐ N5903	Gloster Gladiator II (G-GLAD)	'40
☐ N4877	Avro Anson I (G-AMDA) [VX-F]	'38
☐ V3388	Airspeed Oxford I (G-AHTW)	'40
☐ 'V6028'	Bristol Bolingbroke IVT (G-MKIV)	§ '42
☐ 'V9545'	Westland Lysander IIIA →	
	(G-BCWL) [BA-C]	c42
☐ 'V9673'	Westland Lysander III (G-LIZY) [MA-J]	c43
☐ Z2033	Fairey Firefly I (G-ASTL) [275]	'44
☐ 'Z7381'	Hawker Hurricane XII →	
	(G-HURI) [XR-T]	c43
☐ EP120	V-S Spitfire V → (G-LFVB) [AE-A]	'42
☐ FE695	NA Harvard IIB → (G-BTXI) [94]	US '42
☐ FE992	NA Harvard IIB → (G-BDAM) [K-T]	US '42
☐ HM580	Cierva C.30A (G-ACUU)	Sp '34
☐ KB889	Avro Lancaster X (G-LANC) [NA-I]	'44
☐ 'KD345'	Vought FG-1D Corsair →	
	(G-FGID) [130]	US '44
☐ KF487	NA Harvard IIB	§ US '45
☐ KZ321	Hawker Hurricane IV (G-HURY)	§ '43
☐ LZ766	Percival Proctor III (G-ALCK)	'44
☐ MH434	V-S Spitfire IX → (G-ASJV) [SZ-9]	'43
☐ ML407	V-S Spitfire Tr IX → (G-LFIX) [OU-V]	'44
☐ ML417	V-S Spitfire IX → (G-BJSG) [21-T]	'44
☐ ML796	Short Sunderland MR.5	'44
☐ MV293	V-S Spitfire XIV → (G-SPIT) [OI-C]	'45
☐ NF370	Fairey Swordfish II	'44
☐ PK624	V-S Spitfire F.22 [RAU-T]	'45
☐ RK858	V-S Spitfire IX	'44
☐ SM832	V-S Spitfire XIV → (G-WWII) [YB-A]	'44
☐ TA719	DH Mosquito TT.35 (G-ASKC) [6T]	'45
☐ TG528	HP Hastings C.1A	'47
☐ TV959	DH Mosquito T.3 [AF-V]	§ '45
☐ TX226	Avro Anson C.19	'46
☐ VN485	V-S Spitfire F.24	'45
☐ VX653	Hawker Sea Fury FB.11 (G-BUCM)	'49
☐ 'WF714'	Gloster Meteor F.8 (WK914)	§ '53
☐ WH725	EE Canberra B.2	'53
☐ WJ945	Vickers Varsity T.1 (G-BEDV) [21]	'53
☐ WK991	Gloster Meteor F.8	'53
☐ WM969	Hawker Sea Hawk FB.5 [10]	'54
☐ WV276	Hawker Hunter F.4 [D]	'55
☐ WZ590	DH Vampire T.11 [19]	'52

☐ XB261	Blackburn Beverley C.1 cockpit	'55
☐ XE627	Hawker Hunter F.6A [T]	'56
☐ XF375	Hawker Hunter F.6 (G-BUEZ) [05]	§ '57
☐ XF708	Avro Shackleton MR.3/3 [C]	'58
☐ XG613	DH Sea Venom FAW.21	'56
☐ XG797	Fairey Gannet ECM.6 [277]	'57
☐ XH648	HP Victor B.1A(K2P)	'59
☐ XH897	Gloster Javelin FAW.9	'58
☐ XJ824	Avro Vulcan B.2	'61
☐ XK936	Westland Whirlwind HAS.7 [62]	US '57
☐ XL587	Hawker Hunter T.7 [Z]	'58
☐ XM135	EE Lightning F.1 [B]	'59
☐ XN239	Slingsby Cadet TX.3 [G]	c57
☐ XP281	Auster AOP.9	'61
☐ XP772	DHC Beaver AL.1 (G-BUCJ)	§ Can '61
☐ XR222	BAC TSR-2	'64
☐ XR241	Auster AOP.9 → (G-AXRR)	'61
☐ XS567	Westland Wasp HAS.1 [434-E]	'64
☐ XS576	DH Sea Vixen FAW.2 [125 -E]	'64
☐ XS863	Westland Wessex HAS.1	US '65
☐ XV474	McDD Phantom FGR.2 [T]	US '70
☐ XZ133	HS Harrier GR.3 [10]	'75
☐ A-549	FMA Pucara	Arg c76
☐ 'A19-144'	Bristol Beaufighter 21	'44
☐ BB201-103	Heinkel (CASA) 2-111	Gr 'c53
☐ E3B-153	Bücker (CASA) 1-131E Jungmann →	
	(G-BPTS) [781-75	Gr '34
☐ Fv35075	SAAB J35A Draken	Swn c60
☐ J-4021	Hawker Hunter F.58 (G-BWIU)	'59
☐ J-4031	Hawker Hunter F.58 → (G-BWFR)	'59
☐ J-4058	Hawker Hunter F.58 → (G-BWFS)	'59
☐ J-4066	Hawker Hunter F.58 → (G-BXNZ)	'59
☐ J-4090	Hawker Hunter F.58 → (G-JIAL)	'59
☐ J-4105	Hawker Hunter F.58 (G-BWOU)	'56
☐ NZxxxx	NA AT-6D Texan → (LN-AMY)	US '44
☐ NZ5648	Vought FG-1D Corsair → (NX55JP)	US '44
☐ 'P-8196'	Curtiss P-40M Warhawk → (G-KITT)	US '42
☐ 'S3398'	SPAD S.XIII repro (G-BFYO) [1]	Fr '18
☐ 06	Dewoitine D.27 → (F-AZJD)	Sws c33
☐ '20'	Lavochkin La-11	§ Ru c45
☐ 57	Dassault Mystère IVA [8-MT]	Fr '55
☐ '69'	Yakovlev Yak-50 → (G-BTZB)	Ru c77
☐ 243	Hawker Fury ISS → (G-BTTA)	'49
☐ 316	Max Holste Broussard (F-GGKR)	§ Fr c55

English Electric Lightning F.1A XM135 is displayed in the 'Tiger' colours of 74 Squadron. Ken Ellis

☐ 501	MiG MiG-21PF 'Fishbed-D'	Ru c64
☐ 959	MiG MiG-21SPS 'Fishbed-H'	Ru c67
☐ '1164'	Beech 18 3TM → (G-BKGL)	§ US '46
☐ 1190	Messerschmitt Bf 109E-3	Gr '40
☐ 1211	MiG MiG-17 'Fresco' (G-BWUM)	Ru c55
☐ 1408	PZL Mielec TS-11 Iskra	Pol c68
☐ 1747	NA Harvard IV (G-BGPB)	§ c44
☐ 3794	MiG MiG-15 (S-102)	§ c52
☐ 6247	MiG MiG-15UTI (SBLim-2A) →	
	(G-OMIG)	Ru c55
☐ 8178	NA F-86A Sabre →	
	(G-SABR) [FU-178]	US '48
☐ 96+21	Mil Mi-24 'Hind-D' (406)	Ru c79
☐ 9893	Bristol Bolingbroke IVT	§ '42
☐ 10639	Messerschmitt Bf 109G-2	
	(G-USTV) [6]	§ Gr '43
☐ 14286	Lockheed T-33A 'T-Bird'	US '51
☐ 18393	Avro Canada CF.100 Mk.IVB	
	(G-BCYK)	Can '55
☐ 21714	Grumman F8F-2P Bearcat →	
	(G-RUMM) [201]	US '45
☐ '40467'	Grumman F6F-5K Hellcat →	
	(G-BTCC) [19]	US '43
☐ '42161'	Lockheed T-33A-3 Silver Star →	
	(G-TBRD)	US c54
☐ 42165	NA F-100D Super Sabre [VM]	US '54
☐ 60689	Boeing B-52D Stratofortress	US '56
☐ 66692	Lockheed U-2CT	US '56
☐ 69327	Grumman TBM-3E Avenger	
	(CF-KCG) [X-3]	US '44
☐ 80425	Grumman F7F-3P Tigercat →	
	(N7235C) [WT-4]	US '44
☐ 100143	Focke-Achgelis Fa 330A-1	Gr c43
☐ 121752	Grumman F8F-2 Bearcat →	
	(N800H) [106]	US '45
☐ '124485'	Boeing B-17G Flying Fortress →	
	(G-BEDF) [DF-A]	US '45
☐ 126922	Douglas AD-4NA Skyraider →	
	(G-RAID) [AK-402]	US c50
☐ 155529	McDD F-4J(UK) Phantom [114]	US '67
☐ 166328	Hispano HA-1112 Buchon →	
	(G-BOML) [3]	Sp c52
☐ 0-17899	Convair VT-29B-CO Samaritan	§ US '51
☐ 191660	Messerschmitt Me 163B-1 Komet [3]	Gr '44
☐ '217786'	Boeing PT-17 Kaydet	
	(CF-EQS) [25]	US '41
☐ '226413'	Republic P-47D Thunderbolt	
	(N47DD) [UN-Z]	US '44
☐ '226671'	Republic P-47D\N Thunderbolt →	
	(NX47DD) [MX-X]	US '44

☐	'231983' Boeing B-17G Flying Fortress (F-BDRS) [IY-G]	US '45
☐	251457 Con B-24D Liberator nose	US '42
☐	252983 Schweizer TG-3A glider (N66630)	US '42
☐	269097 Bell P-63A Kingcobra → (G-BTWR)	US '43
☐	315509 Douglas C-47A Skytrain (G-BHUB) [W7-S]	US '43
☐	431171 NA B-25J Mitchell (N7614C)	US '44
☐	461748 Boeing TB-29A Superfortress (G-BHDK) [Y]	US '44
☐	463209 NA P-51D Mustang FSM [WZ-S]	US '44
☐	'463221' NA P-51D Mustang → (G-BTCD) [G4-S]	US '44
☐	'472218' NA Mustang 22 → (G-HAEC) [WZ-1]	US '45
☐	'2106449' NA 'P-51C' Mustang → (N51PR)	US c41
☐	48-0292 NA F-86A Sabre (N196B) [FU-242]	US '48
☐	51-7545 NA T-28A Fennec → (N14113)	US '51
☐	52-8521 NA Harvard 4 → (G-TVIJ) [TA-521]	US '52
☐	67-0120 GD F-111E Aardvark	US '67
☐	72-1447 GD F-111E Aardvark cockpit	US '72
☐	77-0259 Fairchild A-10A Thunderbolt II [AR]	US '77
☐	– Amiot AAC.1 Toucan (Ju 52) (6316) [IZ+NK]	Gr c49
☐	– Bücker Bü 133C Jungmeister → (G-AYSJ) [LG+01]	Gr c38

☐	– DH Tiger Moth frame	§ c41
☐	– Fieseler Fi 103 (V-1) on launch ramp (BAPC.93)	Gr c44
☐	– Hawker Hunter F.6 nose (N-250)	'57
☐	– Hawker Hurricane II	c40
☐	– Hawker Typhoon cockpit	c42
☐	– Lavochkin La-9 (G-BWUB)	§ Ru c44
☐	– Mitsubishi A6M 'Zero'	Ja c42
☐	– MS.502 Criquet (EI-AUY) [CF+HF]	Fr c51
☐	– MS.505 Criquet → (G-BPHZ) [TA+RC]	Fr c55
☐	– NA Harvard IIB (B-168)	US '42
☐	– NA Mitchell II → (N88972) [VO-B]	US '43
☐	– NA Yale	§ US '40
☐	– Nakajima Ki-43 Hyabusa	Ja c43
☐	– Yakovlev 'Yak-3U' (G-BWOE)	Ru c44

Nearby:

Audley End House (and miniature railway), *6 miles.*
Cambridge Museum of Technology, *8 miles.*
City of Cambridge, *8 miles*
Shuttleworth Collection, *20 miles – see page 21.*
Stondon Motor Museum, *18 miles – see page 23.*
Stretham Old Engine House, *18 miles.*
Wimpole Home Farm, *6 miles.*

Dewoitine D.27 F-AZJD operated by the Old Flying Machine Company. Ken Ellis

LUDHAM CONTROL TOWER AND MILITARY MUSEUM

Ludham, Norfolk

Address: Ludham Control Tower and Military Museum, Malthouse Lane, Ludham, Norfolk.
Telephone: 01692 678251.
Where: North east of Ludham, north of the A1062 Hoveton-Potter Heigham road.
Open: Daily 10am to dusk, April to September. October to March at weekends 10am to 4pm.
By bus: Details from TIC.
By rail: Wroxham and Hoveton, 6 miles.
Tourist: Hoveton* 01603 782281. Norwich 01603 666-71, Fax: 01603 765389.
Admission: Adult £1.50, child £1.00.
Facilities: Toilets/Parking/Cafe*/Shop*.

The former control (or watch) tower at the aerodrome has been restored and is open to public inspection. Many artefacts have been gathered, including transport items displayed in the grounds. Two airframes are currently held, the cockpit section of a Hawker Tempest V Series I is similar to the Typhoons that once flew from the airfield. The Invader nose section is from a rare Vietnam-era aircraft, reworked for the counter-insurgency role by the On Mark company.

Aircraft exhibit

☐ 417657	Douglas B-26K Invader nose (N99218)	US '45
☐ –	Hawker Tempest V cockpit	c45

Nearby:

Bure Valley Railway, Hoveton, *14 miles.*
City of Norwich: *12 miles.*
City of Norwich Aviation Museum, *12 miles – see page 19.*
Norfolk and Suffolk Aviation Museum, *20 miles – see page 17.*
Station 146 Control Tower Museum, Seething, *16 miles – see page 22.*

Moment of truth. The prototype DH Mosquito, W4050, makes its first flight, 25th November 1940. MAP

MOSQUITO AIRCRAFT MUSEUM

London Colney, Herts

Address: PO Box 107, Salisbury Hall, London Colney, near St Albans, Herts, AL2 1BU.
Telephone: 01727 822051.
Where: At Salisbury Hall, on the B556 west of the South Mimms services (junction of A1/M25). Access off M25 junction 22 (signposted).
Open: March to the end of October, Tuesdays, Thursdays and Saturdays 2pm to 5.30pm, Sundays and Bank Holidays 10.30am to 5.30pm. Last admission 4.30pm.
By bus: No 84 from St Albans to New Barnet stops at end of drive.
By rail: St Albans 4 miles.
Tourist: St Albans 01727 864511, Fax: 01727 863533.
Admission: Adult £4, child/OAP £2, family ticket £10.
Facilities: Toilets/Parking/Shop/Disabled/All/ Brochure.

Now also known as the **de Havilland Heritage Museum**, it is set in the grounds of Salisbury Hall (*not* available for inspection) the museum is devoted to the history of the de Havilland company and associated operations, including Airspeed. The Hall was used as a satellite design and development facility for nearby Hatfield airfield during the war and indeed the prototype Mosquito was built here (see opposite). As well as the large aircraft display hall, there is a workshop and an engine display room plus static aircraft park. Several aircraft are in 'working' order (undercarriage retraction, wing folding etc) and there are days when these are put through their paces. Two aircraft are held on the former Hatfield airfield and can only be viewed 'from afar' for the time being.

Aircraft exhibits:

☐ D-IFSB	DH Dove 6	'53
☐ F-BGNX	DH Comet 1XB fuselage	'53
☐ G-ABLM	Cierva C.24 autogyro	'31
☐ G-ADOT	DH Hornet Moth	'35
☐ G-AFOJ	DH Moth Minor	'39
☐ G-AKDW	DH Dragon Rapide	'44
☐ G-ANRX	DH Tiger Moth crop duster	'39
☐ G-AOTI	DH Heron 2D	§ '53
☐ G-AREA	DH Dove 8	§ '60
☐ G-ARYC	HS.125 Srs 1	'62
☐ G-AVFH	HS Trident 2 nose	'68
☐ G-AWZO	HS Trident 3B-101	§ '72
☐ W4050	DH Mosquito I prototype	'40
☐ LF789	DH Queen Bee (BAPC.186) [R2-K]	c43
☐ TA122	DH Mosquito FB.6 [UP-G]	'45
☐ TA634	DH Mosquito TT.35 [8K-K]	'45
☐ TJ118	DH Mosquito TT.35 nose	'45
☐ WM729	DH Vampire NF.10 nose	'52
☐ WP790	DHC Chipmunk T.10 (G-BBNC) [T] Can '52
☐ WR539	DH Venom FB.4 [F]	§ '56
☐ WX853	DH Venom NF.3	'55
☐ XG730	DH Sea Venom FAW.22 [499-A]	'57
☐ XJ565	DH Sea Vixen FAW.2 [127-E]	'60
☐ XJ772	DH Vampire T.11 [W]	'55
☐ XK695	DH Comet C.2(R) nose	'56
☐ J-1008	DH Vampire FB.6	c55
☐ –	DH Comet 2 nose	'54
☐ –	Hatfield Toucan man-powered aircraft , frame (BAPC.146)	'72
☐ –	Airspeed Horsa I / II fuselage (BAPC.232)	'43

Nearby:

Blake Hall, *20 miles – see page 8.*
Central London, *16 miles.*
Hatfield House, *6 miles.*
North Weald Airfield Heritage Museum, *20 miles – see page 18.*
RAF Museum, Hendon, *10 miles – see page 40.*
Verulamium Roman Town, *6 miles.*

The Muckleburgh Collection is one of the few places that a Harrier GR.3 can be viewed. David S Johnstone

MUCKLEBURGH COLLECTION
Weybourne, Norfolk

Address: Weybourne Camp, Weybourne, Norfolk, NR25 7EG.
Telephone: 01263 588210, Fax: 01263 588425.
Where: Signposted off the A149 west of Cromer.
Open: Mid-March to October 10am to 5pm daily and weekends only winter 10am to 5pm.
By bus: Coastal bus service from Sheringham.
By rail: Sheringham 3 miles.
Tourist: Sheringham* 01263 824329. Cromer 01263 512497.
Admission: Adult £4, OAP £3, child £2, family ticket £10.50.
Facilities: Toilets/Parking/Cafe/Shop/Disabled/Kids/All/Changes/Brochure.

Located on the site of the former Weybourne Military Camp is Britain's largest private military collection including over 100 military vehicles and armoured fighting vehicles from the UK and abroad including the former USSR, Kuwait, Syria, and the Falklands. Other exhibitions include the tank hall, a yeomanry exhibition, First World War photographs and flying equipment. Tank demonstrations take place every Sunday and daily during the school holidays. For a small extra charge there are rides in a six-wheel US Gama Goat amphibious carrier. As well as the airframes, the museum has Bloodhound and a Thunderbird surface-to-air missiles.

Aircraft exhibits:

☐ WD686	Gloster Meteor NF.11		'52
☐ XN967	Blackburn Buccaneer S.1 nose [103]		'63
☐ XZ968	HS Harrier GR.3 [3G]		'82
☐ –	Fieseler Fi-103 (V-1) FSM		Gr '44

Nearby:
City of Norwich Aviation Museum, *20 miles – see page 17.*
Cromer, *6 miles.*
North Norfolk Railway, *2 miles.*
Thursford Steam Museum, *8 miles.*
Wells and Walsingham Light Railway, *10 miles.*

NORFOLK AND SUFFOLK AVIATION MUSEUM

Flixton, Suffolk

Address: The Street, Flixton, near Bungay, Suffolk, NR35 1NZ or Huby Fairhead, 48 Monks Cottages, Langley, Norwich, Norfolk, NR14 8DG.

Telephone: 01986 896644 during museum opening hours.

Where: On the B1062 south west of Bungay.

Open: Easter to October, Sun and Bank Holidays 10am to 5pm; July to August Tuesday, Wed and Thur 10am to 5pm.

By bus: Services to Bungay 2 miles.

By train: Beccles 8 miles.

Tourist: Beccles* 01502 713196. Diss 01379 650523, Fax: 01379 31141.

Admission: Free, donations welcomed.

Facilities:
Toilets/Parking/Cafe*/Shop/Disabled*/All/ Changes/Brochure.

Well established and growing collection of aircraft and artefacts illustrating the development of avia-

tion in general and in particular World War Two flying from Norfolk and Suffolk under the banner of 'East Anglia's Aviation Heritage Centre'. Within the museum is the Royal Observer Corps Museum dedicated to telling the story of the Corps from its earliest days up to its 'stand down'. Good display of artefacts including much from surrounding USAAF bases with particular emphasis on the 446th Bomb Group, who flew from Bungay. Large display and restoration hangar.

Aircraft exhibits:

☐	CDN	EoN Primary glider (BGA.1461)	c62
☐	G-AZLM	Cessna F.172L fuselage	US '71
☐	G-BDVS	Fokker F-27 Friendship 200 cockpit	Neth '63
☐	G-MTFK	Flexiform Striker microlight	'87
☐	'P8140'	V-S Spitfire FSM (BAPC.71) [ZP-K]	'40
☐	VL349	Avro Anson C.19 [V7-Q]	'46
☐	VX580	Vickers Valetta C.2	'50
☐	WF128	Percival Sea Prince T.1	'52
☐	WF643	Gloster Meteor F.8 [X]	'51
☐	WH840	EE Canberra T.4	'54
☐	WV605	Percival Provost T.1 [T-B]	'54

A unique reminder of a bygone flying-boat era. Nose section of a Felixstowe F.5. Ian Hancock

☐ XG329	EE Lightning F.1	'59
☐ XG518	Bristol Sycamore HR.14	'55
☐ XG523	Bristol Sycamore HR.14 cockpit	'55
☐ XH892	Gloster Javelin FAW.9R [J]	'60
☐ XJ482	DH Sea Vixen FAW.1 [713-VL]	'58
☐ XK624	DH Vampire T.11 [32]	'56
☐ XM279	EE Canberra B(I).8 nose	'59
☐ XN304	Westland Whirlwind HAS.7 [F]	US '60
☐ XR485	Westland Whirlwind HAR.10 [Q]	US '64
☐ A-528	FMA Pucara	Arg c76
☐ 79	Dassault Mystère IVA [2-EG]	Fr '55
☐ 42196	NA F-100D Super Sabre	US '54
☐ 54433	Lockheed T-33A 'T-Bird' [TR-433]	US '55
☐ 146289	NA T-28C Trojan (N99153) fuselage	US '53
☐ –	Bensen B.7 gyroglider (BAPC.147)	US c55
☐ –	Felixstowe F.5 forward fuselage	'18
☐ –	Fokker D.VIII scale rep (BAPC.239)	Gr '18
☐ –	Mignet HM.14 Flying Flea (BAPC.115)	
		Fr c36
☐ –	Wallbro Monoplane repro (G-BFIP)	'09

Nearby:
Caister Castle Car Collection, *20 miles.*
City of Norwich Aviation Museum, *18 miles –*
see page 19.
East Anglia Transport Museum, *12 miles.*
Ludham Control Tower, *20 miles – see page 14.*
Motor Museum and Zoo, Banham, *17 miles.*
Station 146 Control Tower Museum, Seething,
8 miles – see page 22.
Steam Museum, Buckenham, *12 miles.*
100th BG Museum, Thorpe Abbotts, *10 miles –*
see page 24.
391st BG Museum, Framlingham, *18 miles –*
see page 25.

NORTH WEALD AVIATION HERITAGE MUSEUM
North Weald, Essex

Address: *Ad Astra* House, Hurricane Way, North
Weald Aerodrome, Epping, Essex, CM16 6AA.
Telephone: 01992 523010 or 01992 560690.
Where: North Weald Bassett, on the B181 south
east of Harlow, junction 7 M11. *Off* Hurricane
Way, entrace to which is from North Weald
village and *not* the aerodrome entrance.
Open: Saturdays and Sundays noon to 5pm.
Other times by arrangement.
By bus: Buses from Epping, Harlow and
Chipping Ongar.
By rail: Epping Underground, Central Line, or
Harlow rail.
Tourist: Chelmsford 01245 283400, Fax: 0124
354026. Saffron Walden 01799 510444.
Admission: £1 or £5 annual membership.
Facilities: Toilets/Parking/Shop/All/Changes/
Brochure.

An extensive collection telling the rich history of
North Weald airfield. The museum is located in a
building near the main gate of what was the Battle
of Britain station. Large array of artefacts in three
rooms spanning 1916 to the present day.

Also:
On North Weald airfield is the **Aces High Flying
Museum** with a large array of aircraft, many of
which have 'starred' in films, eg Douglas Dakota III
N147DC, MiG-21PF 'Fishbed' 503 etc. Viewable by
prior permission, contact: Aces High, North Weald
Aerodrome, Epping, Essex, CM16 6AA.

Nearby:
Central London, *20 miles.*
Blake Hall, *3 miles – see page 8.*
Hatfield House, *18 miles*
Mosquito Aircraft Museum, *20 miles –*
see page 15.
Museum of Artillery, *18 miles – see page 39.*
RAF Museum, *20 miles – see page 40.*
Thameside Aviation Museum, *20 miles –*
see page 24.

CITY OF NORWICH AVIATION MUSEUM

Norwich Airport, Norfolk

Address: Old Norwich Road, Horsham St Faith, Norwich, Norfolk, NR10 3JE.

Telephone: 01603 625309 – recorded message out-of-hours.

Where: Close to Norwich Airport, access from the A140 Cromer Road – signed.

Open: April to October: Tuesday to Saturday 10am to 5pm. Closed Mondays, except Bank Holidays when noon to 5pm. November to March Sat, Sun, Wed 10am to 4pm. Closed 21st December to 2nd January.

By rail: Norwich 3 miles.

Tourist: Norwich 01603 666071, Fax: 01603 765389.

Admission: Adult £2, child/OAP £1 – includes admission to at least one aircraft, normally the Herald airliner.

Facilities: Toilets/Parking/Cafe/Shop/Disabled/All /Changes/Brochure.

On the edge of Norwich Airport – affording views of the comings and goings – the City of Norwich Aviation Museum has a varied aircraft park. Dominating this is the Vulcan and visitors can climb up into the cockpit when staffing levels permit. Emphasis of the internal displays are the history of Norwich Airport when it was RAF Horsham St Faith, military aviation in the area, on wartime life in and around Norwich and on aerial VCs. During 1997 a new extension was opened dedicated to the fascinating operations of 100 Group, courtesy of the 100 Group Memorial Museum Association.

Aircraft exhibits:

☐ G-ASKK	HP Herald 211		'63
☐ WK654	Gloster Meteor F.8		'52
☐ 'XF383'	Hawker Hunter F.51 (E-409) [G]		'56
☐ XH767	Gloster Javelin FAW.9 [A]		'59
☐ XM612	Avro Vulcan B.2		'64
☐ XP355	Westland Whirlwind HAR.10 (G-BEBC) [A]		US '62
☐ XP458	Slingsby Grasshopper TX.1		§ '63
☐ –	V-S Scimitar F.1 nose		c59
☐ 121	Dassault Mystère IVA [8-MY]		Fr '55
☐ 16718	Lockheed T-33A 'T-Bird'		US '51

Nearby:

City of Norwich, *3 miles.*

Ludham Control Tower and Military Museum, *12 miles – see page 14.*

Motor Museum and Zoo, Banham, *20 miles.*

Muckleburgh Collection, *20 miles – see page 16.*

Norfolk & Suffolk Aviation Museum, *18 miles – see page 17.*

Station 146 Control Tower Museum, Seething, *14 miles – see page 22.*

Steam Museum, Buckenham, *9 miles.*

100th Bomb Group Museum, *20 miles – see page 24.*

A reconstruction of an Anderson air raid shelter is a popular exhibit at Norwich. *Ken Ellis*

Above: **One of the detailed displays at the City of Norwich Aviation Museum, covering the wartime RAF in Norfolk.**
Below: **Shuttleworth's well-known Gloster Gladiator has taken on Norwegian Air Force colours.** Both Ken Ellis

SHUTTLEWORTH COLLECTION

Old Warden, Bedfordshire

Address: Old Warden Aerodrome, Biggleswade, Beds, SG18 9ER.

Telephone: 01767 727288, 24 hour information hot-line 0891 323310, Fax: 01767 627745.

Where: East of the B658, west of Biggleswade. Well signposted, including from the A1.

Open: Daily throughout the year, but is closed for up to 14 days covering Xmas Eve, and up to and including New Year's Day. Open April to October 10am to 5pm, November to March 10am to 4pm, the hangar displays are closed one hour after the last admission time.

By rail: Biggleswade 3 miles.

Tourist: Bedford 01234 215226 (and Fax).

Admission: Adult £6, child/OAP/cons £4. Family ticket £15. Different prices apply on flying days.

Facilities: Toilets/Parking/Cafe/Shop/Disabled/Kids/All/Brochure.

Classic historic aircraft, the majority airworthy, nestled amid a delightful grass airfield – the Shuttleworth Collection has long had a heady atmosphere. There are five hangars containing the 'fleet' along with many supporting displays, including the age of airships, flying clothing and engines. A workshop allows visitors to monitor the restoration of collection aircraft. The garage and coachroom houses the impressive collection of vintage cars. On 'normal' days visitors might well be able to see light aircraft visiting the airfield, but the collection stages a series of flying days and evenings* during the summer season when many of the unique resident types take to the air and are joined by modern day military machines, 'warbirds' and other performers. The collection is also host to various fly-ins, classic and veteran car rallies, radio control model flying days and much more.

* Additional charges apply.

Aircraft exhibits:

☐ G-EAGA	Sopwith Dove ✈	'20
☐ G-EBHX	DH Humming Bird ✈	'23
☐ G-EBIR	DH.51 ✈	'25
☐ G-EBJO	ANEC II ultralight	'24
☐ G-EBLV	DH Moth ✈	'25
☐ G-EBWD	DH.60X Moth ✈	'28
☐ G-AAIN	Parnall Elf II ✈	'29
☐ G-AAPZ	Desoutter	'31
☐ G-AAYX	Southern Martlet	'31
☐ G-ABAG	DH Moth ✈	'30
☐ G-ABVE	Arrow Active II ✈	'32
☐ G-ABXL	Granger Archaeopteryx – taxiable	'30
☐ G-ACSS	DH.88 Comet [34] taxiable	'33
☐ G-ACTF	Comper Swift ✈	'32
☐ G-ADGP	Miles Hawk Speed Six ✈	'35
☐ G-AEBB	Mignet HM.14 Flying Flea taxiable	Fr '36
☐ G-AEXF	Percival Mew Gull ✈	'37
☐ G-AFCL	BA Swallow II ✈	'37
☐ G-CAMM	Hawker Cygnet repro ✈	'24
☐ 'C4918'	Bristol M.1C repro (G-BWJM)	'17
☐ D8096	Bristol F.2b Fighter ✈ (G-AEPH)	'18
☐ F904	RAF SE.5A ✈ (G-EBIA)	'18
☐ H5199	Avro 504K ✈ (G-ADEV)	'20
☐ K1786	Hawker Tomtit ✈ (G-AFTA)	'29
☐ K3215	Avro Tutor ✈ (G-AHSA)	'31
☐ K4235	Cierva (Avro 671) C.30A (G-AHMJ) taxiable	Sp '37
☐ 'K5414'	Hawker Hind (Afghan) ✈ (G-AENP)	c37
☐ 'N6181'	Sopwith Pup ✈ (G-EBKY)	'18
☐ 'N6290'	Sopwith Triplane ✈ (G-BOCK)	'17
☐ P6382	Miles Magister I ✈ (G-AJDR)	'40
☐ T6818	DH Tiger Moth II ✈ (G-ANKT)	'40
☐ 'V9441'	Westland Lysander III ✈ (G-AZWT) [AR-M]	'42
☐ W9385	DH Hornet Moth ✈ (G-ADND) [YG-L]	'36
☐ Z7015	Hawker Sea Hurricane I ✈ (G-BKTH) [7-L]	'41
☐ AR501	Sup Spitfire V ✈ (G-AWII) [NN-A]	'42
☐ XA241	Slingsby Grasshopper TX.1	'51
☐ '423'	Gloster Gladiator I ✈ (G-AMRK)	'37
☐ 7198/18	LVG C.VI ✈ (G-AANJ - 9239M)	Gr '18
☐ –	Blackburn Monoplane ✈ (G-AANI)	'12

☐ –	Blake Bluetit (BAPC.37)		§ c33
☐ –	Blériot XI ✈ (G-AANG)		Fr '10
☐ –	Bristol Boxkite replica ✈ (G-ASPP)		'10
☐ –	Deperdussin Mono ✈ (G-AANH)		Fr '10
☐ –	English Electric Wren ✈ (G-EBNV)		'23
☐ –	Roe Triplane IV replica ✈ (G-ARSG)		'10

Also:

Next door is the famed Swiss Garden, one of the major gardens in the country.

Nearby:

City of Bedford, *8 miles.*

Watch Tower Museum, Bassingbourn –
see page 26.

Woburn Abbey and Safari Park, *14 miles.*

Imperial War Museum, Duxford, *20 miles –
see page 10.*

Luton Airport, (with spectator facilities), *16 miles.*

Santa Pod Raceway, *16 miles.*

Stondon Transport Museum, *5 miles – see page 23.*

The Shuttleworth Collection includes a fascinating array or historic cars and carriages. Ken Ellis

STATION 146 TOWER MUSEUM
Seething, Norfolk

Address: Jim Turner, *The Beeches*, Brooke Road, Seething, Norwich, NR15 1DJ.

Telephone: 01508 550288

Where: East of the B1332, north of Bungay. South of Seething village, access from the Thwaite St Mary road, south of the airfield.

Open: First Sunday of each month, May to October 10am to 5pm.

By bus: Details from TIC.

By rail: Norwich, 10 miles.

Tourist: Norwich 01603 666071, Fax: 01603 765389.

Admission: Free, donations welcomed.

Facilities: Toilets/Parking/Cafe*/Shop*/Disabled*/Changes/Brochure

The original wartime control tower at Seething, home to the US 448th Bomb Group, flying Consolidated B-24 Liberators, 1943-44, has been restored and now holds museum in their memory. A wide array of artefacts, including uniforms and other memorabilia combine to bring the history of this large base alive. The airfield is still used by the Waveney Flying Group and good views of any flying activity can be had from the tower.

Nearby:

Ludham Control Tower and Military Museum, *16 miles – see page 14.*

Norfolk & Suffolk Aviation Museum, Flixton – *8 miles – see page 17.*

City of Norwich Aviation Museum, Norwich Airport, *14 miles – see page 19.*

100th BG Museum, *13 miles – see page 24.*

390th BG Museum, *20 miles, see page 25.*

STONDON TRANSPORT MUSEUM & GARDEN CENTRE

Lower Stondon, Bedfordshire

Address: Station Road, Lower Stondon, Henlow, Beds, SG16 6JN.

Telephone: 01462 850339

Where: Signed off the A600 Hitchin to Henlow road.

Open: Daily, 10am to 5pm.

By bus: Details from TIC.

By rail: Hitchin, 5 miles.

Tourist: Bedford 01234 215226 (and Fax).

Admission: Adult £3, Child £1, family £7.

Facilities: Toilets/Parking/Cafe*/Shop*/ Disabled*/All/Changes/Brochure

A superb collection of 260 plus motor vehicles and other transport artefacts arranged in five halls.

There are many other items of interest, including a full-scale replica of HMS *Endeavour* plus armoured cars and other military items. Plans include the setting up of a circuit so that the exhibits can be put through their paces. There are regular meetings of car clubs. The garden centre is well stocked and offers a wide array of suitable diversions!

Aircraft exhibits:

☐	'G-ADRY'	Mignet HM.14 Flying Flea (BAPC.77)	Fr '35
☐	G-AXOM	Penn-Smith gyroplane	'70
☐	XN341	SARO Skeeter AOP.12	'60

Nearby:

Luton Airport (with spectator facilities), *10 miles*.

Shuttleworth Collection, *5 miles – see page 21.*

Watch Tower Museum, Bassingbourn, *14 miles – see page 26.*

Woburn Abbey and Safari Park, *12 miles.*

Contrasting exhibits at Stondon; Skeeter helicopter, AA patrol motorcycle combination and London taxi. Ken Ellis

THAMESIDE AVIATION MUSEUM

East Tilbury, Essex

Where: At Coalhouse Fort, on an unclassified road, east of Tilbury
Open: Open on the last Sunday of the month from 12.30pm and at other times by arrangement.
By rail: Tilbury 3 miles.
Tourist: Thurrock 01708 863733, Fax: 01708 862440.
Facilities: Parking/X

A small collection established in a coastal defensive point overlooking the Thames estuary. Apart from the airframes, the collection centres upon a large amount of material from 'digs' on wreck sites in and around Essex.

Aircraft exhibits:

☐ G-AVZO	Beagle Pup 100 fuselage		'67
☐ B-163	NA Harvard IIB		US '42
☐ 0446	MiG MiG-21UM nose		Ru c72

Nearby:

Blake Hall, *20 miles – see page 8*.
Chatham Dockyard, *10 miles*.
North Weald Airfield Heritage Museum, *20 miles – see page 18*.
Southend-on-Sea, *14 miles*.

100TH BOMB GROUP MEMORIAL MUSEUM

Thorpe Abbotts, Norfolk

Address: 100th BG Association, Common Road, Dickleburgh, Diss, Norfolk, IP21 4PH.
Telephone: 01379 740708.
Where: Signed off the A143, east of Diss.
Open: Open Sat, Sun and Wed and Bank Holidays 10am to 5pm May to September. Open April and October Sat and Sun 10am to 5pm. Closed November to January.
By rail: Diss 5 miles.
Tourist: Diss 01379 650523, Fax: 01508 31141.
Admission: Free, donations appreciated.
Facilities: Toilets/Parking/Shop/Disabled*/All/ Changes/Brochure.

The museum is centred around the restored control tower on what was home to the USAAF's famous *Bloody Hundredth* Bomb Group. A superb and well presented series of displays take the visitor through life on an American bomber base, while telling the specific tale of Thorpe Abbotts. The runways may have gone, but the feeling of nostalgia when looking out from the top of the control tower is enormous. Other original World War Two buildings contain further displays including restored engines and items from local crash sites. Special events and reunions are frequently staged.

Nearby:

Banham Motor Museum and Zoo, *10 miles*.
Bressingham Steam Museum & Railways, *8 miles*.
City of Norwich, *18 miles*.
City of Norwich Aviation Museum, *20 miles – see page 19*.
Mechanical Music Museum, Cotton 12, *18 miles*.
Museum of East Anglia Life, Stowmarket, *20 miles*.
Norfolk & Suffolk Aviation Museum, *10 miles – see page 17*.
Station 146 Control Tower Museum, Seething, *13 miles – see page 22*.
Thetford Wildlife Park, *20 miles*.
390th Bomb Group Memorial Museum, *14 miles – see page 25*.

390TH BOMB GROUP MEMORIAL AIR MUSEUM

Parham, Suffolk

Address: Colin Durrant, Chairman, 101 Avondale Road, Ipswich, Suffolk, IP3 9LA.

Telephone: 01473 711275.

Where: North of the A12 to the east of Saxmundham, signposted.

Open: 11am to 6pm on Sundays and Bank Holidays March through to October. Other times by prior appointment.

By bus: Eastern Counties service Ipswich-Aldeburgh runs close to the museum.

By rail: Saxmundham 4 miles.

Tourist: Aldeburgh* 01728 453637. Ipswich 01473 258070, Fax: 01473 250951.

Admission: Free, donations welcomed.

Facilities: Toilets/Parking/Cafe/Shop/Disabled/All/Brochure.

Based upon the restored control tower of USAAF Station 153, housing the Boeing B-17 Flying For- tresses of the 390th Bomb Group, a vast amount of material has been carefully gathered together to present a history of the base, the unit and of the activities of the 3rd Air Division. Many artefacts have been collected from local crash sites, including a Merlin engine. Restoration of an early Douglas DC-3 is underway. Newly opened is the British Resistance Museum, charting the largely unheard of work of the Auxiliary Units, who would have staged behind the lines covert actions had Britain been invaded.

Aircraft exhibit:

☐ N4565L	Douglas DC-3-201A	US '39

Nearby:

Mechanical Music Museum, Cotton, *16 miles.*

Museum of East Anglia Life, Stowmarket, *20 miles.*

Norfolk & Suffolk Aviation Museum, *18 miles – see page 17.*

100th Bomb Group Museum, *14 miles.*

Station 146 Control Tower Museum, Seething, *20 miles – see page 22.*

Woodbridge Tide Mill & Sutton Hoo, *8 miles.*

The restored control tower at Parham looks out on the former 390th BG's dispersals. **Ken Ellis**

ALSO
IN EAST ANGLIA

Located within RAF Cardington, south of Bedford, the **AIRSHIP HERITAGE TRUST** has a display room. Fascinating display on the history of airships, especially relating to Cardington where the huge airship sheds still stand. The Trust also maintains a display at the Shuttleworth Collection – see page 21. Access to the display room by prior arrangement only. Send SAE to G/C P A Garth, 5 Orchard Lane, Brampton, Huntingdon, Cambridgeshire, PE1 8TF.

BASSINGBOURNE TOWER MUSEUM within Allenbrooke Barracks, Bassingbourne, Cambridgeshire. Restored watch tower devoted in great detail to the history of the former airfield, including the 91st Bomb Group and the RAF's 11 OTU and 231 OCU, operated by the East Anglian Aviation Society. Visits by prior arrangement only. Send SAE to Mike Killaspy, 3 Stainfoin Close, Sawston, Cambs, CB2 4JY.

Within the grounds of the Alexanders International Language School – the former RAF Bawdsey Manor – the **BAWDSEY RADAR MUSEUM** has been established within the former prototype Chain Home transmitter blockhouse to tell the story of the birth of radar. The museum is in the fledgling stage, with occasional open days. There are plans to take in the adjacent former Bloodhound SAM site. Send SAE to Bawdsey Radar Museum, Bawdsey Estate Office, near Woodbridge, Ipswich, Suffolk, IP12 3AZ.

HATFIELD GALLERIA, this huge shopping and leisure mall suspended over the A1M at Hatfield displays a full-scale model of the DH.88 Comet racer G-ACSS (BAPC.257) *Grosvenor House* (the 'real' G-ACSS is at the Shuttleworth Collection – see page 21. There's an 'open-air' coffee bar just under it and the shops could form a useful 'trade-

off'. A short walk to the south is *The Comet*, 1930s public house and on the road to Hatfield town centre to the east list *The Airfield* – a new pub with a DH Vampire on the inn sign. To the west lies the forlorn and empty former British Aerospace factory.

LAKENHEATH VISITOR CENTRE AND MEMORIAL PARK. A striking memorial to the exploits of the United States Air Force in Europe has been established within the base with an F-4C Phantom II, F-15A Eagle and F-111E Aardvark dramatically displayed. Viewable by prior permission only from the Officer Commanding.

The **BLYTH VALLEY AVIATION COLLECTION**, an expanding collection of aircraft and artefacts at Walpole, Suffolk (including six nose sections and EE Lightning F.3 XR718) holds occasional open days but is also viewable by prior arrangement. Send SAE to Cliff Aldred, *Vulcan's End*, Mells Road, Walpole, Halesworth, Suffolk, IP19 0PL.

The **VULCAN RESTORATION TRUST** looks after the static Avro Vulcan B.2 XL426 at Southend Airport, Essex. Supporters club and regular magazine. Occasional open days, when the airframe goes 'live', otherwise visits by prior arrangement only. Contact: Richard Clarkson, 39 Breakspears Drive, St Pauls Cray, Orpington, Kent, BR5 2RX.

Note:

The **REBEL AIR MUSEUM** at Earls Colne, Essex, closed Spring 1997. **No.39 RESTORATION GROUP** at North Weald, Essex, disbanded during late 1997.

HEART OF ENGLAND

Gloucestershire, Herefordshire & Worcestershire, Shropshire, Staffordshire, Warwickshire and the West Midlands.

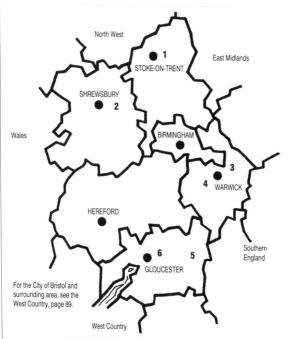

North West

1
STOKE-ON-TRENT

East Midlands

SHREWSBURY
2

BIRMINGHAM

Wales

3
4 WARWICK

HEREFORD

6
GLOUCESTER 5

Southern England

For the City of Bristol and surrounding area, see the West Country, page 89.

West Country

1 The Potteries Museum & Art Gallery
2 Aerospace Museum
3 Midland Air Museum

4 Wellesbourne Wartime Museum
5 Wellington Museum & Art Gallery
6 Jet Age Museum

Heart of England Tourist Board
Woodside, Larkhill Road, Worcester, WR5 2EF
Tel: 01905 763436 Fax: 01905 763450

AEROSPACE MUSEUM
Cosford, Shropshire

Address: Cosford, Shifnal, Shropshire, TF11 8UP.
Telephone: 01902 374112 or 01902 374872,
Fax: 01902 374813. Web-site:
http://www.rafmuseum.org.uk/flat/cosford/
Where: On the A41 south east of Shifnal, signed
off Junction 3, M54.
Open: Daily 10am to 5pm with the exception of
Xmas and New Year, last admission 4pm.
By bus: Services to Albrighton from
Wolverhampton and Telford.
By rail: Cosford Halt – walking distance.
Tourist: Ironbridge 01952 432166, Fax: 01952
432204. Telford 01952 291370, Fax: '291723.
Admission: Adult £5.00, OAP £4.00, Child £3.00,
Family Ticket £13.00.
Facilities: Toilets/Parking/Cafe/Shop/Disabled/
All/Changes/Brochure.

Opening during the summer of 1998 is the prestigious Aviation and Heritage Training Centre which will expand still further the facilities on site. The Aerospace Museum is really five-in-one museums

Prototype and development line-up, left to right:
Hunting 126, SARO SR.53 and BAC TSR.2. Ken Ellis

with the transport aircraft collection including the British Airways exhibits; the world-renowned missile collection; the research and development aircraft collection, the warplane collection and the engine collection. Set in 25 acres within RAF Cosford – the museum affords views of activity on the airfield. There are three huge display halls and an impressive open air static park, dominated by the transport collection including the Short Belfast, the largest aircraft in regular museum care in Great Britain. Airliner exhibits are opened to the public on various occasions. The museum stages regular special events and exhibitions, including a Flight Activities week during the autumn school half-term where visitors can sit in a variety of aircraft; and the annual open day and airshow.

Aircraft exhibits:

☐ G-AAMX	DG.60GM Moth	c32
☐ G-AEEH	Mignet HM.14 Flying Flea	Fr '36
☐ 'G-AFAP'	Junkers (CASA) 352L (T2B-272)	Gr c52
☐ 'G-AJOV'	Westland Dragonfly HR.3 (WP495)	US '52
☐ G-AMOG	Vickers Viscount 701	'53
☐ G-AOVF	Bristol Britannia 312F	'58
☐ G-APAS	DH Comet 1XB	'53
☐ G-APFJ	Boeing 707-436	US '59
☐ G-ARPH	HS Trident 1C	'64

☐ G-ARVM	Vickers VC-10 Srs 1101		'63
☐ G-AVMO	BAC 111-510ED		'67
☐ K4972	Hawker Hart Trainer		'35
☐ 'K7271'	Hawker Fury II FSM (BAPC.148)	§	'31
☐ DG202/G	Gloster F.9/40 Meteor		'42
☐ HS503	Fairey Swordfish IV (BAPC.108)	§	'44
☐ 'KG374'	Douglas Dakota IV (KN645) [YS]	US	'44
☐ 'KL216'	Republic P-47D Thunderbolt (13064) [RS-L]	US	'45
☐ KN751	Consolidated Liberator VI	US	'45
☐ LF738	Hawker Hurricane II [UH-A]		'43
☐ RF398	Avro Lincoln B.2		'45
☐ RW393	V-S Spitfire XVI [XT-A]		'45
☐ TA639	DH Mosquito TT.35		'45
☐ TG511	HP Hastings T.5		'48
☐ TS798	Avro York C.1		'45
☐ TX214	Avro Anson C.19		'46
☐ VP952	DH Devon C.2/2		'47
☐ VX461	DH Vampire FB.5	§	'48
☐ VX573	Vickers Valetta C.3	§	'49
☐ WA634	Gloster Meteor T.7 ejection seat test-bed		'49
☐ WD931	EE Canberra B.2 nose		'51
☐ WE600	Auster C4 'Antarctic'		'51
☐ WE982	Slingsby Prefect TX.1		'50
☐ WG760	EE P.1A		'54
☐ WG768	Short SB.5		'52
☐ WG777	Fairey FD-2		'56
☐ WK935	Gloster Meteor F.8 prone pilot test-bed		'53
☐ WL679	Vickers Varsity T.1		'53
☐ WL732	BP Sea Balliol T.21		'54
☐ WP912	DHC Chipmunk T.10		'52
☐ WS843	Gloster Meteor NF.14 [Y]	§	'54
☐ WV562	Percival Provost T.1 [P-C]		'54
☐ WV746	Percival Pembroke C.1		'55
☐ WZ744	Avro 707C		'53
☐ XA564	Gloster Javelin FAW.1		'55
☐ XA893	Avro Vulcan B.1 nose		'56
☐ XD145	SARO SR.53		'56
☐ XD674	Hunting Jet Provost T.1		'54
☐ XE670	Hunter F.4 nose		'55
☐ XF785	Bristol 173 Srs 1	§	'52
☐ XF926	Bristol T.188		'63
☐ XG337	EE Lightning F.1		'59
☐ XH171	EE Canberra PR.9 [U]		'58
☐ XH672	HP Victor K.2		'60
☐ XJ918	Bristol Sycamore HR.14		'56
☐ XK724	Folland Gnat F.1		'56
☐ XL703	SAL Pioneer CC.1		'56
☐ XL993	SAL Twin Pioneer CC.1		'58
☐ XM555	SARO Skeeter AOP.12	§	'60
☐ XM598	Avro Vulcan B.2		'63
☐ XN714	Hunting 126		'63
☐ XP411	AW Argosy C.1		'62
☐ XR220	BAC TSR-2		'65
☐ XR371	Short Belfast C.1		'65
☐ XR977	Folland Gnat T.1		'66
☐ XS639	HS Andover E.3A		'66
☐ XV591	McDD Phantom FG.1 nose	US	'70
☐ XW547	HS Buccaneer S.2B		'72
☐ XX765	SEPECAT Jaguar GR.1 XX765 fly-by-wire test-bed		'74
☐ A-515	FMA Pucara (ZD485)	Arg	c76
☐ J-1704	DH Venom FB.4		c55
☐ L-866	Con PBY-6A Catalina	US	'45
☐ 204	Lockheed SP-2H Neptune	US	'53
☐ 5439	Mitsubishi Ki 46-III 'Dinah'	Ja	'45
☐ 6130	Lockheed Ventura II	US	'42
☐ '6771'	Republic F-84F Thunderstreak [FU-6]	US	'52
☐ 112372	Messerschmitt Me 262A-2a	Gr	'44
☐ 191614	Messerschmitt Me 163B-1a Komet	Gr	'44
☐ 420430	Messerschmitt Me 410A-1-U2 Hornisse [3U+CC]	Gr	'43
☐ 475081	Fieseler Fi 156C-7 Storch	Gr	'42
☐ –	Fieseler Fi 103 (V-1) flying-bomb (BAPC.94)	Gr	c44
☐ –	Focke-Achgelis Fa 330A-1 rotorkite	Gr	c44
☐ –	Hawker P.1121 fuselage	§	'58
☐ –	Kawasaki Ki 100-1b (BAPC.83)	Ja	'45
☐ –	Sopwith Camel repro (BAPC.59)		'18
☐ –	Yokosuka MXY7 Ohka 11 (BAPC.99) suicide weapon	Ja	c45

Nearby: Ironbridge Gorge Industrial Museums, 8 miles. Severn Valley Railway, 16 miles.

JET AGE MUSEUM
Gloucestershire Airport, Staverton, Glos

Address: Hangar 7, Gloucestershire Airport, West Camp, Cheltenham Road Estate Glos GL2 9QY.

Telephone: 01452 715100.
E-mail: noel.gac@argonet.co.uk. Web-site: http://www.argonet.co.uk/users/noel.gac

Where: On the west side of Gloucestershire Airport (signed from the M5 and A40), access on B4063.

Open: Daily (inc Bank Holidays) 11am to 4pm.

By bus: No.94 from Gloucester, every 10 mins.

By train: Gloucester or Cheltenham, both 5 miles.

Tourist: Gloucester 01452 421188, Fax: 01452 504273. Cheltenham 01242 522878, Fax: 01242 515535.

Admission: Adult £3.00, child/cons £1.50.

Facilities:
Toilets/Parking/Cafe/Shop/Disabled/Brochure

Run by the Gloucestershire Aviation Collection, the museum at Staverton is by way of a 'transit stop' as the aim is to return to Hucclecote – now the Gloucester Business Park – to establish a permanent museum at the birthplace of the jet, where the Gloster E28/39 was built. As well as the airframes and a wide array of artefacts there is a viewing and picnic area that offers commanding views of the activity at the airport. A reproduction Gloster Gamecock biplane fighter is underway and visitors can monitor its progress. The collection aims to show the history and development of jet aircraft and of aviation in Gloucestershire in general.

Aircraft exhibits:

☐	'V7767'	Hawker Hurricane fsm (BAPC.72)	'40
☐	VM325	Avro Anson C.19	'47
☐	WF784	Gloster Meteor T.7	'51
☐	WK126	EE Canberra TT.18	'54
☐	WS807	Gloster Meteor NF.14	'53
☐	XG331	EE Lightning F.1 nose	'59
☐	XG691	DH Sea Venom FAW.22	'55
☐	XH903	Gloster Javelin FAW.9	'58
☐	XM569	Avro Vulcan B.2 nose	'63
☐	XV165	HS Buccaneer S.2B nose	'66
☐	XW264	HS Harrier T.2 nose	'69
☐	XX889	HS Buccaneer S.2B	'75
☐	–	Gloster Gamecock repro (BAPC.259)	'25
☐	–	McBroom Arion hang-glider	c74

Nearby:
Cities of Cheltenham and Gloucester, *each 5 miles.*

Gloucester and Warwickshire Railway, *8 miles.*

National Birds of Prey Centre, Newent, *10 miles.*

Wellington Museum and Aviation Gallery, *18 miles – see page 35.*

Gloster Gamecock I J7910 flying from Hucclecote. Jet Age are building a faithful Gamecock reproduction. MAP

MIDLAND AIR MUSEUM
Coventry Airport, Warwickshire

Address: Baginton, Coventry, CV8 3AZ.
Telephone: 01203 301033 plus Fax.
Where: Signed from the A45/A423 junction to the south west of Coventry city centre.
Open: Open daily 10.30am to 5pm.
By bus: Metro Bus Service, T route.
By rail: Coventry 3 miles.
Tourist: Coventry 01203 832303 or 01203 832304, Fax: 01203 832370.
Admission: Adult £3, OAP £2.25, Child £2, Family ticket £8.50.
Facilities: Toilets/Parking/Cafe/Shop/Disabled/ All/Changes/Brochure/X.

Overlooking Coventry airport and offering good views of the activity there, the museum provides an 'then' to the airport's 'now'. Inside the excellent display hall – the Frank Whittle Jet Heritage centre traces the history of the jet engine and a vivid display charting the development of the turbojet and Whittle's key role. The 'Wings over Coventry' display highlights the area's contribution to the development of aviation through the many companies that have built aircraft locally. The static aircraft park has over 25 exhibits, with some available for internal inspection on special days. The museum has developed an aerospace education centre in association with local colleges and schools. Special events are staged.

Aircraft exhibits:

☐	G-EBJG	Parnall Pixie III ultralight	§ '26
☐	G-ABOI	Wheeler Slymph ultralight	§ '31
☐	G-AEGV	Mignet HM.14 Flying Flea	Fr '36
☐	G-ALCU	DH Dove 2	'47
☐	G-APJJ	Fairey Ultra Light helicopter	'58
☐	G-APRL	AW Argosy 101	'59
☐	G-APWN	Westland Whirlwind Srs 3	US '59
☐	G-ARYB	HS.125 Srs 1	'62
☐	G-MJWH	Chargus Vortex 120 hang glider	'83

☐	BGA.804	Slingsby Cadet TX.1 (VM589)	§ '48
☐	'A7317'	Sopwith Pup repro (BAPC.179)	'17
☐	EE531	Gloster Meteor F.4	'46
☐	'JR505'	Hawker Typhoon Ib cockpit	'43
☐	VF301	DH Vampire F.1 [RAL-G]	'46
☐	VS623	Percival Prentice T.1 (G-AOKZ)	'49
☐	VT935	BP 111A delta research aircraft	'50
☐	VZ477	Gloster Meteor F.8 nose	'49
☐	WF922	EE Canberra PR.3	'53
☐	WH646	EE Canberra T.17A nose [EG]	'52
☐	WS838	Gloster Meteor NF.14	'54
☐	WV797	Hawker Sea Hawk FGA.6	'54
☐	XA508	Fairey Gannet T.2 [627-GN]	'54
☐	XA699	Gloster Javelin FAW.5	'57
☐	XD626	DH Vampire T.11	'54
☐	XE855	DH Vampire T.11 nose	§ '54
☐	XF382	Hawker Hunter F.6A [15]	'55
☐	XJ579	DH Sea Vixen FAW.2 nose	'58
☐	XK741	Folland Gnat F.1 fuselage	'55
☐	XK907	Westland Whirlwind HAS.7 cockpit	US '57
☐	XL360	Avro Vulcan B.2	'62
☐	XN685	DH Sea Vixen FAW.2	'61
☐	XR771	EE Lightning F.6 [BM]	'66
☐	ZF598	EE Lightning T.55	'67
☐	E-425	Hawker Hunter F.51	'56
☐	R-756	Lockheed F-104G Starfighter	US c62
☐	70	Dassault Mystère IVA	Fr '55
☐	17473	Lockheed T-33A 'T-Bird'	US '51
☐	24535	Kaman HH-43B Huskie	US '62
☐	29640	SAAB J29F	Sw '52
☐	37699	McDD F-4C Phantom	US '63
☐	70270	Mc Donnell F-101B Voodoo cockpit	US '57
☐	280020	Flettner Fl 282V Kolibri frame	Gr '44
☐	51-4419	Lockheed T-33A 'T-Bird'	US '51
☐	54-2174	NA F-100D Super Sabre	US '54
☐	56-0312	McDonnell F-101B Voodoo	US '56
☐	58-2062	DHC U-6A Beaver	Can '58
☐	63-7414	McDD F-4C Phantom	US '63
☐	–	Bristol Beaufighter cockpit	c43
☐	–	Crossley Tom Thumb homebuild (BAPC.32)	§ '37
☐	–	Druine Turbulent (BAPC.126)	c64
☐	–	Humber Monoplane repro (BAPC.9)	'12

Part of the aircraft park at the Midland Air Museum, Sea Hawk FGA.6 WV797 in the foreground. John Wickenden

Also at Coventry Airport:

The airport is the headquarters for Atlantic Airlines who operate a wide fleet of types on freighting, charter and specialist aerial work. Within their structure is the well-known **Air Atlantique 'Historic Flight'** who operate a series of aircraft that appear at events all over the UK offering pleasure flights or performing at airshows. Aircraft operated include: Percival Prentice 1 VR259 (G-APJB), Avro Anson C.21 WD413 (G-VROE) SAL Twin Pioneer 3 XT610 (G-APRS) and a Douglas Dakota from the main fleet. As well as being seen 'away' at events, Air Atlantique stages regular 'Enthusiast Days' during the summer season when tours of the engineering hangar and pleasure flights are undertaken. These are *very* popular and operate strictly on a prior booking arrangement. Details on 01203 307566.

Nearby:

Bosworth Battlefield and Market Bosworth Light Railway, *20 miles.*

City of Coventry (and Cathedral), *3 miles.*

Heritage Motor Museum, Gaydon, *14 miles.*

Percy Pilcher Museum, *14 miles – see page 56.*

Wellesbourne Wartime Museum, *14 miles – see page 34.*

THE POTTERIES MUSEUM AND ART GALLERY

Stoke-on-Trent, Staffordshire

Address: Bethesda St, Hanley, Stoke, ST13DW.
Telephone: 01782 232323, Fax: 01782 205033.
Where: In Bethesda Street, off Broad Street, Hanley. Use junction 15 from M6.
Open: Daily 10.30am to 5pm Monday to Saturday and Sundays 2pm to 5pm.
By bus: Hanley bus and coach station close to.
By rail: Stoke-on-Trent 2 miles.
Tourist: Stoke 01782 284600.
Admission: Free.
Facilities: Toilets/Parking/Cafe/Shop/Disabled/ All/Changes/Brochure.

On April 18, 1998 the Stoke-on-Trent Museum and Art Gallery changes its name to better reflect the area that it serves. Reginald J Mitchell, the designer of the Spitfire, was born in Stoke and with the Spitfire as a centre-piece, the museum has a display devoted to one of its famous sons. Other subjects on exhibition include natural history, archaeology, social history, fine art, decorative art and an incredible ceramics collection. Special events organised – details from the museum.

Aircraft exhibit:

☐ RW388	V-S Spitfire XVI [U4-U]		'45

Also: The museum is part of the Potteries Heritage Trail that takes in 20 venues all linked by tourist 'brown signs' and a detailed leaflet. Also an hourly minibus link – The China Service – connecting up Stoke's major china attractions. (Leaflet and more details available from the Stoke-on-Trent TIC.)

Nearby:
Alton Towers, *14 miles.*
Brindley Water Mill, Leek, *10 miles.*
Cheddleton Railway Centre, *8 miles.*
Foxfield Steam Railway, *6 miles.*
Jodrell Bank Radio Telescope, *16 miles.*

The Potteries Museum's Spitfire XVI during its days as 'gate guardian' at RAF Andover, the mid-1960s. MAP

WELLESBOURNE WARTIME MUSEUM

Wellesbourne Mountford, Warwickshire

Address: Derek Powell, 167 Colebourne Road, Kingsheath, Birmingham, B13 0HB.
Where: South of Wellesbourne Mountford village, follow signs to the airfield.
Open: Sundays and Bank Holidays 10am to 4pm.
By rail: Stratford-upon-Avon 4 miles.
Tourist: Stratford-upon-Avon 01789 293127, Fax: 01789 295262.
Admission: Adult £1.50, Child 50p.
Facilities: Disabled*/All/Changes/Brochure.

A fascinating museum with many of the displays inside the airfield's former underground battle headquarters - a unique venue. Should an invasion have taken place, the operations and defence of the airfield would have been conducted from this armoured complex. Displays inside the underground bunker and 'on-surface' are largely devoted to the history of Wellesbourne Mountford

airfield, the home of 22 OTU during the Second World War. Excellent reconstructions include the cockpit of a Spitfire including working gun sight and the turret area from a Blenheim. Both the Vampire and the Sea Vixen are available for internal inspection and work in progress on the Provost is viewable. The airfield is an active general aviation centre and the comings and goings can be seen to advantage from the museum.

Aircraft exhibits:

☐ WV679	Percival Provost T.1 [O-J]		'54
☐ XJ575	DH Sea Vixen FAW.2 nose		'59
☐ XK590	DH Vampire T.11 [V]		'56
☐ –	McBroom Argus hang-glider		'74

Nearby:

City of Coventry, *16 miles.*
Heritage Motor Museum, Gaydon, *6 miles.*
Midland Air Museum, *14 miles – see page 31.*
Stratford-upon-Avon, *3 miles.*
Warwick Castle, *6 miles.*
Wellington Museum and Art Gallery, Moreton, *14 miles – see page 35.*

Within the underground bunker at Wellesbourne are a fascinating array of displays show what life was like at the wartime airfield. Ken Ellis

WELLINGTON MUSEUM AND AVIATION GALLERY

Moreton-in-the-Marsh, Gloucestershire

Address: British School House, Moreton-in-the-Marsh, Glos, GL56 0BG.

Telephone: 01608 560323.

Where: On the A44 to the west of the village of Moreton-in-the-Marsh.

Open: 10am to 12.30am and 2pm to 5.30pm daily.

By bus: On Worcester-London route and local services to Cheltenham.

By rail: Moreton-in-the-Marsh, walking distance.

Tourist: Chipping Camden* 01386 840101.
Stow-on-the-Wold 01451 831082.
Fax: 01451 870083.

Admission: Adult £1.50. Child 50p.

Facilities: Toilets/Parking/Shop/Disabled*/All/Changes/Brochure.

Gerry Tyack's excellent aviation art and print gallery has expanded to take on a much greater role, not only telling via photographs and artefacts the stories behind some of the paintings and prints on show but including the history of the former local airfield, which was home to 21 OTU and their Wellingtons. Substantial remains from former 20 OTU Wellington L7975 which crashed in Scotland in October 1940 are also held.

Nearby:

Gloucestershire and Warwickshire Railway, *12 miles.*

Heritage Motor Museum, Gaydon, *16 miles.*

Jet Age Museum, *18 miles – see page 30.*

Stratford-upon-Avon, *16 miles.*

Wellesbourne Wartime Museum, *14 miles – see page 34.*

ALSO IN THE HEART OF ENGLAND

The Boulton Paul Association have established the **BOULTON PAUL AIRCRAFT HERITAGE PROJECT** courtesy of Dowty Aerospace at their Wolverhampton plant. As well as an extensive history of 'BP' and aviation in the West Midlands, their is also a workshop undertaking the recreation of Defiant I night fighter N3378 and the restoration of Balliol T.2 trainer WN149. Additionally, other airframes can be found using the workshop facility. Currently open Fridays 2pm to 5pm and the first Sunday of each month, May to October. Other times by prior arrangement. SAE to Boulton Paul Association, 35 Blakeley Avenue, Wolverhampton, WV6 9HR.

BRISTOL AERO COLLECTION (BAC) and the Britannia Aircraft Preservation Trust (BAPT) are now well established at Kemble airfield, south west of Cirencester. BAC are collecting an impressive array of airframes and artefacts to tell the story of the Bristol Aeroplane Company: for example Bristol Scout reproduction N5419, Harrier GR.1 XV798 (Bristol Siddeley Pegasus engine development airframe), missiles and much more, including examples of Bristol-built vehicles. BAPT concentrate on the 'Whispering Giant', the Britannia airliner, with the newly-arrived Series 253 EL-WXE being kept 'live'. Open days planned, otherwise by prior appointment, SAE to: Bristol Aero Collection, PO Box 77, Bristol BS99 7AR.

The **COTSWOLD AIRCRAFT RESTORATION GROUP**, have a workshop within RAF Innsworth, near Cheltenham, with work on several projects underway, including Auster AOP.9 XR267. Restoration projects are also undertaken for other bodies, including GAL Monospar VH-UTH for the Newark Air Museum. Visits by prior arrangement only. Send SAE to: Steve Thompson, *Kia-Ora*, Risbury, Leominster, Herefordshire, HR6 0NQ.

JET AIRCRAFT PRESERVATION GROUP are hard at work on a number of projects at Long Marston airfield, Warwickshire. Included in the collection are a Vampire T.11, Jet Provost T.4 and a Hunter composite that will be finished as an FR.10 - a variant that has otherwise become 'extinct'. Visitors are welcome at weekends when JAPG members are at work on the aircraft. Other times by arrangement, send SAE to : Stewart Holder, 62 Avon Street, Evesham, Worcester, WR11 4LG.

Located in the village of Upper Hill, near Leominster, is **SHEPPARDS SURPLUS AND GARDEN CENTRE**, which includes in its attractions Supermarine Swift F.4 WK275 and Westland Whirlwind HAR.10 XP360. Open all week.

Dominating the entrance to Sheppards Surplus and Garden Centre in the delightful village of Upper Hill is Swift WK275. Ken Ellis

Note:

The **BIRMINGHAM MUSEUM OF SCIENCE AND INDUSTRY** closed in November 1997 and is due to re-open again, on a new site, as the Millennium Point Discovery Centre in 2001.

GREATER LONDON

East Anglia

1

2 3

4

Southern England

South East

1 Royal Air Force Museum
2 Science Museum
3 Imperial War Museum
4 Museum of Artillery

London Tourist Board,
26 Grosvenor Gardens, London, SW1W 0DU
Tel: 0171 7303450 Fax: 0171 7309367

Visitorcall is a service providing pre-recorded information on a wide range of subjects,
dial 0891 505 plus the following numbers for information: **440** What's on in London this week;
462 Museums; **465** Popular attractions; **467** Greenwich and Military Museums;
468 Famous Houses and Gardens – and many more, details from the LTB.

IMPERIAL WAR MUSEUM
South Lambeth

Address: Lambeth Road, London, SE1 6HZ.
Telephone: 0171 416 5320, Fax: 0171 416 5374.
Web-site www.iwm.org.uk
Where: South east of Waterloo Station, off
Kenington Road (the A23).
Open: Open 10am to 6pm daily. Closed 24-26th
December.
By bus: Many services.
By rail: Underground, Lambeth North and
Elephant & Castle; Mainline Waterloo.
Tourist: London 0171 7303450, Fax: 0171
7309367.
Admission: Adult £5.00, Cons £4.00, Child £2.50,
Family ticket £13.00.
Facilities: Toilets/Cafe/Shop/Disabled/All/
Changes/Brochure.

While the vast majority of the Imperial War Museum's aircraft collection is at Duxford (see under

East Anglia), aviation is far from absent in the
famous Lambeth premises. Within the aviation
gallery some of the airframes are posed in dramatic 'flying trim'. The remainder of the museum holds
a wealth of material and all aspects of 20th century
warfare with many 'inter-active' displays and
vibrant presentations. Special events and exhibitions are staged throughout the year, including
presentations aimed specifically at children.

Aircraft exhibits:

☐	2699	RAF BE.2c	'16
☐	N6812	Sopwith Camel 2F1	'18
☐	R6915	V-S Spitfire I	'40
☐	DV372	Avro Lancaster I nose	'43
☐	PN323	HP Halifax A.VII nose	'45
☐	120235	Heinkel He 162A-1	Gr '45
☐	733682	Focke-Wulf FW 190A-8	Gr c43
☐	'472258'	NA P-51D Mustang (44-73979)	
		[WZ-I]	US '44
☐	–	Fieseler Fi 103 (V-1) flying-bomb	
☐		(BAPC.198)	Gr '45
☐	–	Mitsubishi A6M 'Zero' cockpit	Ja c44

Balconies offer a variety of angles on the aircraft and large exhibits in the Imperial War Museum's main gallery.
Spitfire I R6915 in the foreground, BE.2c 2699 in the background. Ken Ellis

Also:
There are two other Imperial War Museum sites in London. **HMS** *Belfast* at Morgan's Lane (London Bridge or Tower Hill Underground), more details on 0171 407 6434 and the **Cabinet War Rooms** in King Charles Street (Westminster or St James's Park Underground), more details on 0171 930 6961.

Old Fred, **the nose of former 467 Squadron Lancaster I DV372 at South Lambeth.** Ken Ellis

Nearby:
Brooklands Museum, *16 miles – see page 71.*
Lambeth Palace, *1 mile.*
Mosquito Aircraft Museum, *20 miles – see page 15.*
Museum of Artillery, *8 miles – see below.*
RAF Museum, *9 miles – see page 40.*
Science Museum, *5 miles – see page 43.*
Shoreham Aircraft Museum, Kent, *16 miles – see page 78.*
Westminster, *2 miles.*

MUSEUM OF ARTILLERY
Woolwich

Address: The Old Royal Military Academy, Woolwich, London, SE18 4JJ.
Telephone: 0181 3165402, Fax: 0181 7815929.
Where: Within the Royal Artillery Institution at The Rotunda, off the A206.
Open: Open Monday to Friday and 1pm to 4pm. Closed Bank Holidays and Public Holidays.
By bus: Several bus services.
By rail: Woolwich Arsenal, walking distance.
Tourist: Greenwich, 0181 858 6376.
Admission: Free.
Facilities: Toilets/Parking/Disabled*/All/Brochure.

Telling the story of artillery from the earliest times to the latest laser and satellite guided weaponry the museum includes within its collection an Auster AOP.9 as an example of 'eyes for the guns'.

Aircraft exhibit:

☐ XR271	Auster AOP.9	'62

Nearby:
Imperial War Museum, *8 miles, see opposite.*
Maritime Trust, Greenwich and Southwark, *3 miles.*
RAF Museum, *14 miles – see page 40.*
Science Museum, *13 miles – see page 43.*
Shoreham Aircraft Museum, Kent, *16 miles – see page 78.*

ROYAL AIR FORCE MUSEUM

Hendon

Address: Hendon, London, NW9 5LL.
Telephone: 0181 2052266, Fax: 0181 2008044.
Event hotline 0181 205 9191.
Web-site: http://www.rafmuseum.org.uk
Where: On Grahame Park Way, signposted from the end of the M1.
Open: 10am to 6pm all week, with the exception of Christmas and New Year.
By bus: No 303 Mill Hill–Colindale–Edgware. Thameslink, Mill Hill.
By rail: Colindale Underground, Northern Line.
Tourist: London 0171 7303450, Fax: 0171 7309367.
Admission: Adult £5.20, Cons £2.60.
Facilities: Toilets/Parking/Cafe/Shop/Disabled/Kids/All/Changes/Brochure/X.

Essentially three museums rolled into one, here is the RAF Museum itself, the Bomber hall and the Battle of Britain Experience, all located on the former and historic Hendon airfield. As well as the aircraft halls there are many galleries – including 'RAF 2000' with a wide-screen presentation of the Eurofighter, always an art or photograph exhibition, 'Plane and Simple' demonstrations on the theory of flight, a free cinema showing classic films and other footage, Tornado flight simulator, TriStar flight deck and a 'Touch and Try' Jet Provost cockpit. The Sunderland flying-boat is equipped with a walkway through its cavernous fuselage. The acclaimed Battle of Britain Experience includes the use of excellent dioramas and 'talking' mannequins giving the perspective of the 'man in the street'. The museum has a vigorous policy of staging special events and exhibitions including the Flight Activities week for younger including workshops for youngsters, simulators and pleasure flying. Note that the RAF Museum has many more aircraft

View of part of the main hall at Hendon. Note the 'Belfast Truss' construction of the First World War period hangars. RAF Museum

on charge than are listed below, these are on loan to other museums (including the bulk of the aircraft at Manchester), under restoration or in store. See also Aerospace Museum Cosford, page 28, which is an RAF Museum site.

Aircraft exhibits:

☐ G-EBMB	Hawker Cygnet	'24
☐ '168'	Sopwith Tabloid repro (G-BFDE)	'14
☐ 433	Blériot XXVII (BAPC.107)	Fr '12
☐ '687'	RAF BE.2b repro (BAPC.181)	'14
☐ '2345'	Vickers Gunbus repro (G-ATVW)	'14
☐ '3066'	Caudron G.III	Fr c16
☐ A301	Morane BB fuselage frame	Fr '15
☐ 'E449'	Avro 504K	c17
☐ F938	RAF SE.5A (G-EBIC)	'18
☐ 'A8226'	Sopwith 1½ Strutter repro (G-BIDW)	'16
☐ 'C4994'	Bristol M.1C repro (G-BLWM)	'17
☐ 'E2466'	Bristol F.2b Fighter (BAPC.165)	'18
☐ F1010	Airco DH.9A	'18
☐ F6314	Sopwith Camel F.1	c17
☐ 'F8614'	Vickers Vimy repro (G-AWAU)	'18
☐ 'J9941'	Hawker Hart (G-ABMR)	'31
☐ K4232	Avro Rota I (Cierva C.30A)	'34
☐ K6035	Westland Wallace II fuselage	'35
☐ K8042	Gloster Gladiator II	'37
☐ L5343	Fairey Battle I [VO-S]	'39
☐ 'L8756'	Bristol Bolingbroke IVT (10001) [XD-E]	'42
☐ N1671	BP Defiant I [EW-D]	'40
☐ 'N5182'	Sopwith Pup replica (G-APUP)	'17
☐ N5628	Gloster Gladiator II fuselage	'39
☐ N5912	Sopwith Triplane	'17
☐ N9899	Supermarine Southampton I fuselage	'25
☐ P2617	Hawker Hurricane I [AF-F]	'40
☐ P3175	Hawker Hurricane I wreck	'40
☐ R5868	Avro Lancaster I [PO-S]	'42
☐ R9125	Westland Lysander III [LX-L]	'40
☐ T6296	DH Tiger Moth II	'41
☐ W1048	HP Halifax II [TL-S]	'42
☐ W2068	Avro Anson I fuselage [68]	'41
☐ X4590	V-S Spitfire I [PR-F]	'40
☐ Z7197	Percival Proctor III	'40
☐ 'BE421'	Hawker Hurricane FSM (BAPC.205) [XP-G]	'41

☐ BL614	V-S Spitfire Vb [ZD-F]	'41
☐ 'DD931'	Bristol Beaufort VIII [L]	'42
☐ FE905	NA Harvard IIB	US '43
☐ 'FX760'	Curtiss Kittyhawk IV [GA-?]	US '43
☐ KK995	Sikorsky Hoverfly I [E]	'44
☐ MF628	Vickers Wellington T.10	'44
☐ 'MH486'	V-S Spitfire FSM (BAPC.206) [FF-A]	'43
☐ ML824	Short Sunderland V [NS-Z]	'44
☐ MN235	Hawker Typhoon IB	'43
☐ MP425	Airspeed Oxford I	'43
☐ PK724	V-S Spitfire F.24	'46
☐ 'PR536'	Hawker Tempest II (HA457) [OQ-H]	'45
☐ RD253	Bristol Beaufighter TF.10	'44
☐ TJ138	DH Mosquito TT.35 [VO-L]	'45
☐ VT812	DH Vampire F.3 [N]	'47
☐ WE139	EE Canberra PR.3	'53
☐ WH301	Gloster Meteor F.8	'51
☐ WZ791	Slingsby Grasshopper TX.1	'58
☐ XB812	NA Sabre F.4 [U]	US '53
☐ XD818	Vickers Valiant BK.1	'56
☐ XG154	Hawker Hunter FGA.9	'57
☐ XG474	Bristol Belvedere HC.1 [O]	'62
☐ XL318	Avro Vulcan B.2	'61
☐ XM463	Hunting Jet Provost T.3A fuselage [38]	'60
☐ XM717	HP Victor K.2 nose	'63
☐ XS925	EE Lightning F.6 [BA]	'67
☐ XV424	McDD Phantom FGR.2 [I]	'69
☐ XW323	BAC Jet Provost T.5A [86]	'70
☐ XX946	Panavia Tornado UK prototype [WT]	'74
☐ XZ997	HS Harrier GR.3 [V]	'82
☐ A2-4	Supermarine Seagull V	'37
☐ A16-199	Lockheed Hudson IIIA (G-BEOX) [SF-R]	US '41
☐ E3B-521	Bücker (CASA) 1-131E Jungmann	Gr c52
☐ HD-75	Hanriot HD.1	Fr '17
☐ MM5701	Fiat CR-42 [13-95]	It '40
☐ 920	Supermarine Stranraer [QN]	'40
☐ 4101	Messerschmitt Bf 109E-3 [12]	Gr '40
☐ 8417/18	Fokker D.VII	Gr '18
☐ 01120	MiG MiG-15bis 'Fagot' (Lim-2)	c55
☐ '34037'	NA TB-25N Mitchell (N9115Z)	US '44
☐ 120227	Heinkel He 162A-2	Gr '45
☐ 360043	Junkers Ju 88R-1 [D5+EV]	Gr c42
☐ '413573'	NA P-51D Mustang (N6526D) [B6-K]	US '44

☐ 494083	Junkers Ju 87D-3 [RI+JK]	Gr c40
☐ 584219	Focke-Wulf Fw 190F-8/U1 [38]	Gr c42
☐ 701152	Heinkel He 111H-23 [NT+SL]	Gr '42
☐ 730301	Me Bf 110G-4/R6 [D5+RL]	Gr c42
☐ 44-83868	Boeing B-17G Flying Fortress [N]	US '44
☐ –	Clarke TWK hang glider (BAPC.100)	'10
☐ –	Fieseler Fi 103 (V-1) (BAPC.92)	Gr c45
☐ –	Hawker Hind (Afghan) (BAPC.82)	c37
☐ –	*Nulli Secundus* airship gondola	'07

Nearby:
Blake Hall, Ongar, *20 miles – see page 8.*
Brooklands Museum, *20 miles – see page 71.*
Central London 8 miles.
Hatfield House 20 miles.
Imperial War Museum, *10 miles – see page 38.*
Mosquito Aircraft Museum, *10 miles –
  see page 15.*
North Weald Airfield Heritage Museum, *20 miles,
  – see page 18.*
Science Museum, *8 miles – see page 43.*

The Battle of Britain Hall at Hendon, nearest the camera is the Messerschmitt Bf 110G-4/R6 night fighter. Alan Curry

SCIENCE MUSEUM
South Kensington

Address: Exhibition Road, South Kensington, London SW7 2DD.
Telephone: 0171 9388080 or 0171 9388008, Fax: 0171 938811.
Web-site: http://www.nmsi.ac.uk/collexh/
Where: Exhibition Road, off Cromwell Road (A4).
Open: Open daily 10am to 6pm, except for 24th-26th December.
By bus: Variety of service.
By rail: South Kensington Underground.
Tourist: London 0171 7303450, Fax: 0171 7309367.
Admission: Adult £5.95, Child/cons £3.20.
Facilities: Toilets/Cafe/Shop/Disabled/Kids/All/Changes/Brochure.

Under the heading 'Flight' the museum's aeronautical gallery is an impressive sight with its overhead walkways, 'stacks' of aero engines and walk-around and through exhibits. All this before the visitor takes in the historic importance of the aircraft exhibits on view, including the first British powered aircraft to fly (the Roe), the first to fly the Atlantic non-stop (the Vimy) and the first British jet aircraft, the Gloster E.28/39). On one wall is a cross section from a scrapped Boeing 747 'Jumbo' jet, putting that world beating aircraft into awesome proportion. Alongside the 'Flight' gallery is 'Flight Lab' where the principals of flight can be explored in a 'hands-on' manner, including a Cessna 150 that youngsters can 'fly'. The remainder of the museum is just as absorbing taking in transport, technology and science. Regular special exhibitions and displays are staged. There is an extensive 'out-station' at Wroughton, Wilts (mentioned in the West Country section) but this is only open by appointment.

A view of the 'Flight' gallery, with Amy Johnson's famous DH.60 Moth G-AAAH *Jason* centre. To the right is the Alcock and Brown Vickers Vimy that was the first to fly the Atlantic non-stop. Science Museum

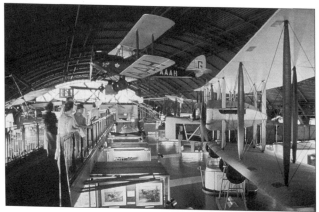

Aircraft exhibits:

☐ G-EBIB	RAF SE.5A		'18
☐ G-AAAH	DH Moth		'28
☐ G-ASSM	HS.125-1-522		'64
☐ G-ATTN	Piccard hot air balloon	§ Sws	'66
☐ G-AWAW	Cessna F.150F	US	'66
☐ G-AZPH	Pitts S-1S	US	'70
☐ G-BBGN	Cameron A-375 balloon gondola	§	'73
☐ DFY	Schempp-Hirth Std Cirrus glider	Gr	'73
☐ OO-BFH	Piccard Gas balloon gondola	§ Sws	'32
☐ 304	Cody Biplane (BAPC.62)		'12
☐ J8067	Westland Pterodactyl I		'28
☐ L1592	Hawker Hurricane I [KW-Z]		'38
☐ P9444	V-S Spitfire IA [RN-D]		'40
☐ S1595	Supermarine S.6B		'31
☐ W4041/G	Gloster E.28/39		'41
☐ AP507	Cierva C.30A (Avro 671) [KX-P]	Sp	'34
☐ KN448	Douglas Dakota IV nose	US	'44
☐ XN344	SARO Skeeter AOP.12		'60
☐ XP831	Hawker P.1127		'60
☐ 210/15	Fokker E.III (BAPC.56)	Gr	'15
☐ 191316	Messerschmitt Me 163B-1 Komet	Gr	'43
☐ 442795	Fieseler Fi 103 (V-1) flying-bomb	Gr	'44
☐ –	Airship No 17 'Beta II' gondola		'10
☐ –	Antoinette VII (BAPC.55)	Fr	'10
☐ –	JAP-Harding Monoplane (BAPC.54)		'10
☐ –	Lilienthal Standard hang glider repro (BAPC.124)	Gr	1895
☐ –	Roe Triplane Type I (BAPC.50)		'09
☐ –	Short Brothers Gas balloon basket		'09
☐ –	Vickers Vimy IV (BAPC.51)		'18
☐ –	Wright Flyer repro (BAPC.53)	US	'03

Nearby:

Brooklands Museum, *16 miles – see page 71.*
Geological Museum next door.
Harrods, *1 mile.*
Mosquito Aircraft Museum, *20 miles – see page 15.*
Natural History Museum next door.
Imperial War Museum, *5 miles – see page 38.*
RAF Museum, *8 miles – see page 40.*
Shoreham Aircraft Preservation Society, *16 miles – see page 78.*
Victoria and Albert Museum next door.

ALSO IN LONDON

On the site of the former **CROYDON AIRPORT**, a growing visitor attraction is emerging, which it is hoped will evolve into a major museum in due course. Located on the A23 in south London, the former terminal building has de Havilland Heron 2D 'G-AOXL' (G-ANUO) mounted dramatically outside, and DH Tiger Moth T7793 displayed within, along with much memorabilia.

By way of other diversions, in **LEICESTER SQUARE** can be found 'Planet Hollywood' with a Wallis WA-116 autogyro marked as *Little Nellie* 'G-ARZB', the famed 'star' of the James Bond film *You Only Live Twice.* Nearby, at the 'Trocadero' as well as all the electronic attractions of Sega World, HS Harrier GR.3 ZD670 is on display.

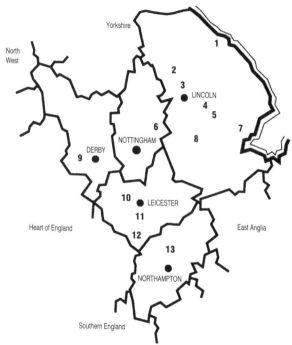

EAST MIDLANDS

Derbyshire, Leicestershire, Lincolnshire, Northamptonshire, Nottinghamshire

Yorkshire

North West

1

2

3 LINCOLN
4
5

7

6

NOTTINGHAM

8

DERBY
9

10 LEICESTER

11

Heart of England

East Anglia

12

13

NORTHAMPTON

Southern England

1 NATO Aircraft Museum
2 Bomber County Aviation Museum
3 Dambusters Heritage Centre
4 Thorpe Camp Visitor Centre
5 Battle of Britain Memorial Flight Visitor Centre

6 Newark Air Museum
7 Lincolnshire Aviation Heritage Centre
8 Lincolnshire Aviation Heritage Trail – Cranwell, see text for others

9 Derby Industrial Museum
10 Snibston Discovery Park
11 British Aviation Heritage
12 Percy Pilcher Museum
13 'Carpetbaggers' & Northants Aviation Museums

East Midlands Tourist Board
Exchequergate, Lincoln, LN2 1PZ. Tel: 01522 531521 Fax: 01522 532501

BATTLE OF BRITAIN MEMORIAL FLIGHT VISITOR CENTRE

RAF Coningsby, Lincolnshire

Address: BBMF Visits, RAF Coningsby, Lincoln, LN4 4SY.

Telephone: 01526 344041.

Where: At RAF Coningsby, south of Coningsby village and signed off the A153.

Open: Monday to Friday except Bank Holidays 10am to 4.30pm with the last guided tour at 3.30pm. Note: although booking is *not* required to attend the Visitor Centre, it is advisable as it may be that the Flight in whole or in part are positioning to a show.

By bus: Services pass through Coningsby from Sleaford and Horncastle.

By rail: Sleaford 14 miles.

Tourist: Sleaford 01529 414294.

Admission: Adult £3, OAP/Children £1.50.

Facilities: Toilets/Parking/Shop/Disabled/All/Changes/Brochure/X.

RAF Coningsby is the home of the Battle of Britain Memorial Flight, famed for their appearances at air events all over the country. The Visitor Centre was established in 1986 so that people could see the aircraft of the Flight 'at home'. During the winter deep maintenance can be seen going on. In addition to the aircraft, there is an excellent historic display within the visitor centre itself. During the summer months, Flight aircraft may well be away and if visitors are intending to see a specific aircraft, it is important to telephone beforehand to check that it/they will be in attendance. The visitor centre is on the North Kesteven Airfield Trail, see page 62.

Aircraft exhibits:

☐ P7350	V-S Spitfire IIA ✈	[BA-Y]	'40
☐ AB910	V-S Spitfire VB ✈	[ZD-C]	'41
☐ LF363	Hawker Hurricane IIC		§ '44
☐ MK356	V-S Spitfire IX ✈	[21-V]	'44
☐ PA474	Avro Lancaster I ✈	[WS-J]	'44
☐ PM631	V-S Spitfire PR.XIX ✈	[S]	'45
☐ PS915	V-S Spitfire PR.XIX ✈	[UM-G]	'45
☐ PZ865	Hawker Hurricane II ✈	(G-AMAU) [J]	'44
☐ WG486	DHC Chipmunk T.10 ✈		Can '51
☐ WK518	DHC Chipmunk T.10 ✈		Can '51
☐ ZA947	Douglas Dakota III✈	[YS-DM]	US '43

Nearby:

Boston, *12 miles.*

City of Lincoln, *20 miles.*

Cranwell Visitor Centre, *15 miles – see page 52.*

Dambusters Heritage Centre, *20 miles – see page 52.*

Lincolnshire Aviation Heritage Centre, *8 miles – see page 51.*

Metheringham Visitor Centre, *10 miles – see page 52.*

Navenby Heritage Room, *16 miles – see page 52.*

Thorpe Camp, *2 miles – see page 58.*

Wellingore Heritage Room, *16 miles – see page 52.*

When the aircraft of the Flight are 'at home', visitors can inspect them up close. Lancaster I PA474.
Ken Ellis

BOMBER COUNTY AVIATION MUSEUM

Hemswell Cliff, Lincolnshire

Address: John Jennings, 14 Steeping Drive, Habrough Park, Immingham, Lincs, DN40 2DS.

Where: Within the former RAF Hemswell (now Hemswell Cliff) north of the A631 Gainsborough to Market Rasen road. Signed from the A631 as Hemswell Antique and Craft Centre.

Open: Sundays and Bank Holidays 11am to 6pm and at other times by prior arrangement.

By rail: Gainsborough 10 miles.

Tourist: Lincoln 01522 529828.

Admission: Free, donations welcomed.

Facilities: Shop/Disabled*/Changes/Brochure.

Within the main site of the former RAF Hemswell, the museum is run by the Hemswell Aviation Society. There is a small internal display and shop and a static aircraft park. Car park and cafe facilities in the huge antique and craft centre, located in the former airmen's accommodation blocks, close by.

Aircraft exhibits:

☐	G-AEJZ	Mignet HM.14 Flying Flea (BAPC.120)	§ Fr '36
☐	WJ975	EE Canberra T.19 [S]	'53
☐	WW388	Percival Provost T.1 [O-F]	'54
☐	XD445	DH Vampire T.11 [51]	'54
☐	'XG193'	Hawker Hunter FGA.9 (XG195)	'56
☐	XG506	Bristol Sycamore HR.14	'55
☐	XM192	EE Lightning F.1A [K]	'61
☐	XP557	Hunting Jet Provost T.4 [72]	'62
☐	101	Dassault Mystère IVA [8-MN]	Fr '55

Nearby:

City of Lincoln, *12 miles*.

Dambusters Heritage Centre, *10 miles* – see page 52.

Metheringham Visitor Centre, *18 miles* – see page 52.

National Mining Museum, Bothamsall, *18 miles*.

Navenby Heritage Room, *20 miles* – see page 52.

Skellingthorpe Heritage Room, *14 miles* – see page 52.

Wellingore Heritage Room, *20 miles* – see page 52.

Displayed at the Bomber County Aviation Museum is Dassault Mystère IVA 101. Roger Richards

BRITISH AVIATION HERITAGE

Bruntingthorpe Aerodrome, Leicestershire

Address: Bruntingthorpe Aerodrome,
Bruntingthorpe, Lutterworth, Leics, LE17 5QH.
Telephone: 0416 2478030.
Where: West of the A50 Leicester to Northampton
road, north east of Lutterworth.
Open: Sundays 10am to 4pm. Other times by
prior appointment.
By rail: Rugby, 10 miles. Leicester, 8 miles.
Tourist: Market Harborough 01858 468106.
Admission: Adult £1.00, Cons £1.00.
Facilities: Toilets/Parking/Disabled*.

A large and varied aviation heritage operation has
been established of a period of years at Bruntingthorpe thanks to the pioneering of the Walton family,
who own the huge site. C Walton (Aviation Division) Ltd have founded British Aviation Heritage
(BAH) and have built up an impressive collection of
aircraft, several of which are maintained in taxiable
condition, including Vulcan B.2 XH558 – the last
Vulcan to fly. Presently a visit involves a guided
tour of the BAH aircraft and others on the airfield,
subject to operating conditions. Special event
days when aircraft are taxied. Aircraft listed below
are BAH owned, or on loan to them.

Aircraft exhibits:

☐	F-BTGV	Aerospacelines Super Guppy 201	US '67
☐	TF-ABP	Lockheed TriStar 1	US '73
☐	XD875	Vickers Valiant B.1 nose	'57
☐	XH537	Avro Vulcan B.2MRR nose	'65
☐	XH558	Avro Vulcan B.2 (G-VLCN)	'60
☐	XM715	HP Victor K.2	'62
☐	XS235	DH Comet 4C	'63
☐	XX900	HS Buccaneer S.2B	'76
☐	85	Dassault Mystère IVA [8-MV]	Fr '55
☐	1018	PZL Mielec TS-11 Iskra	Pol c70

Also on site with regular 'running' days are the
Lightning Preservation Group. Two Lightning
F.6s, XR728 and XS904, are maintained in taxiable
condition. SAE for more details to: LPG, 95 Thorn-
hill, North Weald, Essex, CM16 6DP.

Nearby:

'Carpetbagger' Aviation Museum, *12 miles, see
page 49.*
City of Leicester, *8 miles.*
Midland Air Museum, *18 miles, see page 31.*
Percy Pilcher Museum, *7 miles, see page 56.*
Snibston Discovery Park, *20 miles, see page 57.*

**BAH have started a 'Cold War' collection – founder
member is TS-11 Iskra 1018.** Mark Harris

'CARPETBAGGER' AND NORTHANTS AVIATION MUSEUMS

Harrington, Northamptonshire

Address: Sunny Vale Farm Nursery, off Lamport Road, Harrington, Northampton, NN6 9PF.
Telephone: 01604 686608.
Where: On minor road south out of Harrington village, towards Lamport, and turn right after the A14 underpass – follow signs.
Open: Easter to October at weekends and Bank Holidays, 10am to 5pm (last entry 4.30pm). Other times by prior appointment.
By rail: Market Harborough 5 miles.
Tourist: Market Harborough 01858 468106, Fax: 01858 463168.
Admission: Adult £2, Child £1 – covers both museums.
Facilities: Toilets/Parking/Cafe/Shop/Disabled/All/Changes/Brochure.

Opened in March 1994, this museum is centred upon the Administration Site of what was once USAAF Station 179, home of the clandestine 801st/492nd BGs. Within the hardened Group Operations building is the 'Carpetbagger' Aviation Museum where can be found a wide array of items devoted to the history of the station and the activities of the 'Operation Carpetbagger' Group. The Northamptonshire Aviation Society have set up their museum in the former Paymaster's building, where many fascinating items of equipment and memorabilia are displayed, including the remains of several crashed aircraft from the Second World War recovered from NAS's extensive 'dig' activity.

Nearby:

British Aviation Heritage, *12 miles – see page 48.*
Foxton Locks and Inclined Plane, *8 miles.*
Lamport Hall & Brampton Railway Museum, *4 miles.*
Naseby Battlefield and Farm Museum, *6 miles.*
City of Northampton, *12 miles.*
Percy Pilcher Museum, *12 miles – see page 56.*

Inside the hardened Group Operations building of the 'Carpetbagger' museum. Ken Ellis

DERBY INDUSTRIAL MUSEUM

Derby, Derbyshire

Address: Silk Mill Lane, off Full Street, Derby, DE1 3AR.

Telephone: 01332 255308, Fax: 01332 255804.

Where: South of the inner ring road (the A52), close to the cathedral and well signed.

Open: Monday 11am to 5pm, Tuesday to Saturday 10am to 5pm. Bank Holidays 2pm to 5pm. (Closed Xmas and New Year.)

By bus: Derby's main bus station is a short walk away. By rail: Derby, walking distance.

Tourist: Derby 01332 255802.

Admission: Free.

Facilities: Toilets/Parking/Shop/Disabled/All/Changes/Brochure.

The aero engine gallery – effectively a shrine to local producer Rolls-Royce – is an absorbing and beautifully presented look at development from the Eagle to the mighty RB.211. The museum building, the Silk Mill, was one of the world's first modern factories, originally built in 1718. Other exhibits concentrate on textiles, the iron industry, railways, a working beam engine and many other aspects of Derby's industrial heritage.

Nearby:

Brewery Museum, Burton-on-Trent, *12 miles*.

City of Nottingham, *12 miles*.

Derby city centre, cathedral and museum all close to. River Derwent runs past the museum.

Heights of Abraham, Matlock, *16 miles*.

Snibston Discovery Park, *14 miles – see page 57*.

Tramway Museum, Crich, *12 miles*.

Part of the extensive aero engine gallery at Derby. Ken Ellis

LINCOLNSHIRE AVIATION HERITAGE CENTRE

Address: East Kirkby, near Spilsby, Lincs, PE23 4DE.
Telephone: 01790 763207, Fax: 01790 763677.
Where: On the A155 west of Spilsby, signposted.
Open: Open Easter to October Monday to Saturday 10am to 5pm, last admission 4pm, and November to Easter Monday to Saturday 10am to 4pm, last admission 3pm.
Note – *not* open on Sundays.
By rail: Boston 12 miles.
Tourist: Woodhall Spa* 01507 600206.
Boston 01205 356656.
Admission: Adult £3.50, OAP £3.25, Child £1.50.
Facilities: Toilets/Parking/Cafe/Shop/Disabled/Kids/All/Changes/Brochure.

Using part of the former bomber airfield of East Kirkby, the museum has grown around the well restored and fitted out watch tower. Main centre of attraction is undoubtedly the Lancaster, which performs ground runs occasionally. There are wide-ranging displays dedicated to the men and machines who flew from East Kirkby and from Lincolnshire in general. Other exhibitions include the RAF Escaping Society, military vehicles, an air raid shelter and items excavated by the Lincolnshire Aircraft Recovery Group.

Aircraft exhibits:

☐	AE436	HP Hampden I fuselage	§ '41
☐	BL655	V-S Spitfire V wreck	'42
☐	NP294	Percival Proctor IV [TB-M]	'44
☐	NX611	Avro Lancaster VII (G-ASXX) [DX-C/LE-C]	'45
☐	WH957	EE Canberra E.15 nose	'55
☐	–	Colditz Cock glider repro (BAPC.90)	'44

Nearby:

Battle of Britain Memorial Flight Visitor Centre, *8 miles – see page 46.*
Metheringham Visitor Centre, *16 miles – see page 52.*
Thorpe Camp, *10 miles – see page 58.*

Lancaster VII NX611 occasionally fires up all four Merlins to the delight of visitors. Tony McCarthy

LINCOLNSHIRE AVIATION HERITAGE TRAIL

North Kesteven District Council has developed an award-winning Airfield Heritage Trail around the airfield sites within its boundaries. Most of the sites have been marked with designator signs and information boards. Linking all this together is a well produced booklet describing each site and available from the Sleaford Tourist Information Centre. Additional to this North Kesteven has developed two other centres, one at Cranwell and one at Metheringham which can be visited independently of the trail or used as central points when on it. There are also four heritage rooms within the trail which have sections dealing with the local airfield.

CRANWELL AVIATION HERITAGE CENTRE

Address: c/o Tourist Information Centre, The Mill, Moneys Yard, Carre Street, Sleaford, Lincs, NG34 7TW.
Telephone: 01529 488490, Fax: 01529 413596. E-mail: info@n-kesteven.gov.uk
Where: Signposted just off the A17 (to the south of RAF Cranwell) on the minor road to North and South Rauceby.
Open: Open 9am to 5pm daily (closes 4pm in winter months) other than Xmas and New Year.
By rail: Sleaford 3 miles.
Tourist: The centre is itself a TIC (see number above), or Sleaford 01529 414249.
Admission: Free.
Facilities: Toilets/Parking/Shop/Disabled/All/ Brochure.

Located close to the RAF base, the centre charts the history of Cranwell and gives notes on the other airfields on the Lincolnshire Airfield Trail. Tourist Information Centre adjacent.

Aircraft exhibits:

☐ XE946	DH Vampire T.11 nose	'55
☐ XP556	Hunting Jet Provost T.4 [B]	'61

METHERINGHAM VISITOR CENTRE

Address: As Cranwell.
Telephone: 01526 378270.
Where: At Westmoor Farm, Martin Moor, Metheringham. Signposted off the B1189.
Open: 10am to 5pm April to November, or at other times by appointment.
By rail: Metheringham 1 mile.
Tourist: Sleaford 01529 414249.
Admission: Free.
Facilities: Toilets/Parking/Shop/Disabled/All/ Brochure.

Outside the centre is a memorial garden and an impressive memorial to 106 Squadron. Inside are many displays including rolls of honour and much on the history of the bomber base.

DAMBUSTERS HERITAGE CENTRE: High Street, Scampton (off the A15 north of Lincoln). Adjacent to the Post Office, containing a wealth of material on the famed 617 Squadron, who operated from the now closed base at Scampton for a time. (Telephone: 01522 731333.)

NAVENBY HERITAGE ROOM: Next to the Post Office in Navenby on the A607 south of Lincoln. Open all year 9am to 5.30pm Mon/Tue/Thu/Fri and 9am to 12.30pm Wednesday and Sunday. Exhibits on local history including the RAF in the area.

SKELLINGTHORPE HERITAGE ROOM: Near the Community Centre at Skellingthorpe on the A46, west of Lincoln. Open 10am to 5pm daily April to October and 10am to 4pm November to March. Located in what was the weighbridge office of the former railway station with displays on the former airfield, 50 and 61 Squadrons and F/O Manser VC.

WELLINGORE HERITAGE ROOM: On the A607 in the village, south of Lincoln. Open daily 9am to 5pm. Displays include local airfields, including RAF Wellingore, and local history.

The impressive Royal Air Force College building under construction at Cranwell. This history of this famous Lincolnshire landmark is charted at the Cranwell Aviation Heritage Centre. Ken Ellis collection

NATO AIRCRAFT MUSEUM

New Waltham, Lincolnshire

Address: Grimsby-Cleethorpes Aircraft Preservation Group, 31 Montgomery Road, Cleethorpes, DN35 9JG.

Telephone: 01472 696344 (also Fax).

Where: Peak's Top Farm, New Waltham, south of Grimsby.

Open: Tuesday to Saturday 10am to 5pm.

By rail: Cleethorpes 3 miles.

Tourist: Cleethorpes 01472 200220, Fax: 01472 601404.

Admission: Free, donations appreciated.

Facilities: Parking/Changes/ Brochure.

Operated by the Grimsby-Cleethorpes Aircraft Preservation Group, this growing collection of NATO jets is set amid a decidedly rural environment. As well as the airframes, there is an extensive collection of artefacts, including 'bonedomes' – pilot helmets.

Aircraft exhibits:

☐ XR757	EE Lightning F.6 nose	'65
☐ XR770	EE Lightning F.6 [AA]	'66
☐ XS416	EE Lightning T.5	'64
☐ A-011	SAAB A.35XD Draken	Swn '69
☐ 22+57	Lockheed F-104G Starfighter	US '62

Nearby:

Grimsby and Cleethorpes, *3 miles*.

Grimsby & Louth Light Railway, Ludborough, *5 miles*.

Humber Bridge and Viewing Area, *20 miles*.

Humberside Airport (with viewing facilities), *14 miles*.

NEWARK AIR MUSEUM
Newark, Nottinghamshire

Address: The Airfield, Winthorpe, Newark, Notts,
NG24 2NY
Telephone: 01636 707170.
Where: North east of Newark, off the A46 Lincoln
Road, on Newark Showground. Signposted
from the A1
Open: Daily, excluding December 24th–26th.
April-September weekdays 10am to 5pm,
weekends and Bank Hols 10am to 6pm;
October-March daily 10am to 5pm; November-
February daily 10am to 4pm.
Admission: Adult £3.50, OAPs £2.75, children
£2.00, family ticket £9.00.
By bus: Pathfinder bus to Collingham will drop
near museum.
By rail: Newark Northgate 3 miles
Tourist: Newark 01636 678962, Fax: 01636
612274
Facilities: Toilets/Parking/Cafe/Shop/Disabled/
Kids/All/Changes/Brochure

Located on part of the former RAF Winthorpe airfield, Newark Air Museum celebrates its 25th
anniversary in 1998 and has considerable plans for
expansion. The collection is centred essentially on
post-war RAF aircraft, including a 'speciality' of
Gloster Meteors and on trainer types. Large aircraft
display hall with subsidiary displays including the
history of RAF Winthorpe, Royal Observer Corps,
ejector seats and a Flying Flea 'workshop'.
Restoration workshop on site – visitors can peak at
progress. Engine display hall with extensive collection of piston and jet engines. Phantom, Gnat and
Jet Provost cockpit simulators plus 'JP' nose section available for children to sit in at times. Avro
Shackleton maritime patroller, Avro Vulcan V-
bomber and Handley Page Hastings crew trainer
occasionally open to the public, at extra charge.
The shop is famed for its huge array of model kits.
Special events – details from the museum.

Aircraft exhibits:

☐ G-AGOH	Auster J/1 Autocrat	'45
☐ G-AHRI	DH Dove 1	'48
☐ G-ANXB	DH Heron 1	'55
☐ G-APVV	Mooney M.20A	US c59
☐ G-BFTZ	MS Rallye Club	Fr '67
☐ 'G-MAZY'	DH Tiger Moth	c40
☐ G-MBUE	MBA Tiger Cub 440 microlight	'82
☐ VH-UTH	General Aircraft Monospar ST-12	§ '35
☐ KF532	North American Harvard IIB cockpit	US '44
☐ TG517	Handley Page Hastings T.5	'48
☐ VL348	Avro Anson C.19	'46
☐ VR249	Percival Prentice T.1 [FA-EL]	'48
☐ VZ608	Gloster Meteor FR.9 engine test-bed	'50
☐ VZ634	Gloster Meteor T.7	'49
☐ WB624	DHC Chipmunk T.10	'50
☐ WF369	Vickers Varsity T.1 [F]	'51
☐ WH863	EE Canberra T.17 cockpit	'53
☐ WH904	EE Canberra T.19 [04]	'54
☐ WK277	V-S Swift FR.5 [N]	'55
☐ WM913	Hawker Sea Hawk FB.3 [456-J]	'54
☐ WR977	Avro Shackleton MR.3/3 [B]	'57
☐ WS692	Gloster Meteor NF.12	'53
☐ WS739	Gloster Meteor NF.14	'53
☐ WT651	Hawker Hunter F.1 [C]	'54
☐ WT933	Bristol Sycamore 3	'52
☐ WV606	Percival Provost T.1 [P-B]	'55
☐ WV787	EE Canberra B.2/8	'52
☐ WW217	DH Sea Venom FAW.21 [736]	'55
☐ WX905	DH Venom NF.3	'54
☐ XD593	DH Vampire T.11 [50]	'54
☐ XH992	Gloster Javelin FAW.8	'58
☐ XJ560	DH Sea Vixen FAW.2 [242]	'57
☐ XL149	Blackburn Beverley C.1 cockpit	'57
☐ XL764	Saunders Roe Skeeter AOP.12	'58
☐ XM383	Hunting Jet Provost T.3A [90]	'62
☐ XM594	Avro Vulcan B.2	'63
☐ XM685	Westland Whirlwind HAS.7 [513-PO]	US '58
☐ XN573	Hunting Jet Provost T.3 nose	'61
☐ XN819	Armstrong Whitworth Argosy C.1 cockpit	'61
☐ XN964	Blackburn Buccaneer S.1 [613-LM]	'63

☐	XP226	Fairey Gannet AEW.3 [073-E]	'62
☐	XS417	English Electric Lightning T.5	'64
☐	XT200	Bell Sioux AH.1 (Westland)	US '66
☐	AR-107	SAAB S.35XD Draken	Sw '68
☐	83	Dassault Mystère IVA [8-MS]	Fr '56
☐	'5547'	Lockheed T-33A 'T-Bird' (19036)	US '51
☐	42223	NA F-100D Super Sabre	US '54
☐	56321	SAAB Safir (G-BKPY)	Swn '56
☐	–	Lee Richards Annular Biplane repro (BAPC.20)	§ '11
☐	–	Mignet HM.14 Flying Flea (BAPC.43)	Fr '36
☐	–	Mignet HM.14 Flying Flea fuselage (BAPC.101)	Fr '36
☐	–	Zurowski ZP.1 homebuilt helicopter (BAPC.183)	c75

Also:

Activities of Newark Gliding Club, when weather permits, can be seen to advantage from the museum car park. Newark Showground is host to a wide range of special events during the year, including the six-a-year international antique and collectors fair which is a huge event. During such shows and events a visit to both the showground and the museum is easily achieved.

Nearby:

Belvoir Castle, *14 miles.*
City of Lincoln, *13 miles.*
City of Nottingham, *18 miles.*
Museum of Dolls and Bygone Childhood, Cromwell, *4 miles.*
National Mining Museum, Bothamsall, *14 miles.*
Papplewick Pumping Station and Miniature Railway, *14 miles.*
Cranwell Heritage Centre, *13 miles – see page 52.*
Metheringham Visitor Centre, *16 miles – see page 52.*
Sherwood Forest and Visitor Centre, *14 miles.*

Inside Newark's aircraft exhibition hall, Sea Hawk foremost with the diminutive Tiger Cub microlight 'flying' from the roof structure. Ken Ellis

PERCY PILCHER MUSEUM

Stanford Hall, Leicestershire

Address: Stanford Hall, Lutterworth, Leicestershire, LE17 6DH.
Telephone: 01788 860250, Fax: 01788 860870.
Where: Signposted off an unclassified road east of Swinford, close to junction 19 of the M1 (M6/A14/M1 interchange).
Open: Saturdays and Sundays, Easter to September 2.30pm to 5.30pm, also Bank Hols and the Tuesdays following, same times.
By rail: Rugby 7 miles.
Tourist: Rugby 01788 535348, Fax: 01788 573289.
Admission: House and grounds, Adult £3.80, Child £1.90. Grounds only, including Pilcher Museum, Adult £2.10, Child £1.00.
Facilities: Toilets/Parking/Cafe/Shop/Disabled/All/Brochure/X

Within the stables is a small display devoted to the life and times of Percy Pilcher, including a fine replica of the Hawk glider. Aviation pioneer Pilcher was killed in the grounds of the hall whilst flying the Hawk in September 1899. Also in the stables is an outstanding collection of motorcycles, viewable at extra charge. The 17th century hall is magnificent, the park equally so, boasting the River Avon running through it. Regular special events are staged in the grounds during the season, including occasional balloon rallies.

Aircraft exhibit:

| ☐ – | Pilcher Hawk replica (BAPC.45) | 1896 |

Nearby:
Bosworth Battlefield and Light Railway, *20 miles*.
British Aviation Heritage, *7 miles – see page 48*.
Carpetbagger Aviation Museum, *12 miles – see page 49*.
City of Coventry, *16 miles*.
City of Leicester, *20 miles*.
Midland Air Museum, *16 miles – see page 31*.
City of Northampton, *16 miles*.

Centrepiece of the display to the life and times of Lt Percy Pilcher RN is an excellent reproduction of his Hawk glider. Ken Ellis

SNIBSTON DISCOVERY PARK

Coalville, Leicestershire

Address: Ashby Road, Coalville, Leicestershire, LE6 2LN.

Telephone: 01530 510851, Fax: 01530 813301, 24 hour information line 01530 813256.

Where: Well signed off the A50 Coalville road.

Open: Daily 10am to 6pm, April to October, 10am to 5pm November to March, except December 25-26.

By bus: Midland Fox bus services.

By rail: Loughborough 6 miles.

Tourist: On site, 01530 813608, Fax: 01530 813301.

Admission: Adult £4.75, Child/cons £2.95, Cons £3.25, family ticket £13.50.

Facilities: Toilets/Parking/Cafe/Shop/Disabled/Kids/All/Brochure.

Tracing the history of Leicestershire's industrial heritage in a vivid manner are five galleries: textiles and fashion; engineering; extractive industries; science and transport. In the latter can be found an Auster AOP.9 and a Whittle jet engine, marking the aircraft production and engine pioneering undertaken in the county. Outside is the 100 acre discovery park which includes a colliery tour. Many special events and exhibitions staged during the year.

Aircraft exhibits:

☐ G-AIJK	Auster J/4	§ '46
☐ G-AJRH	Auster J/1N Alpha	§ '47
☐ VZ728	Reid & Sigrist Desford (G-AGOS)	§ '45
☐ XP280	Auster AOP.9	'61

Nearby:

Bosworth Battlefield and Light Railway, *8 miles*.

British Aviation Heritage, *20 miles – see page 48*.

City of Derby, *14 miles*.

Derby Industrial Museum, *14 miles – see page 50*.

Donington Motor Racing Museum, *8 miles*.

City of Leicester, *10 miles*.

City of Nottingham, *16 miles*.

Auster AOP.9 XP280 on display at Snibston, was built at nearby Rearsby, in 1961. Ken Ellis

THORPE CAMP VISITOR CENTRE

Tattershall Thorpe, Lincolnshire

Address: Thorpe Camp Preservation Group, *Lancaster Farm*, Tumby Woodside, Mareham-le-Fen, Boston, PE22 7SP.
Where: On the B1192 south of Woodhall Spa.
Telephone: 01526 342249, Fax: 01526 345249. Web-site: http://www.angelfive.com/ms/thorpecamp
Open: Open Sunday afternoons and Bank Holidays 2pm to 5pm.
By rail: Lincoln 18 miles.
Tourist: Woodhall Spa* 01526 353775, Fax: 01507 600206. Lincoln 01522 529828.
Admission: By donation.
Facilities: Toilets/Parking/Disabled*/ All/ Changes/Brochure.

Located on the former No.1 Communal Site of RAF Woodhall Spa airfield – once base to 617 and 627 Squadrons – this museum charts the history of the airfield and the units that served on it. Other displays include life in wartime Lincolnshire, all supported by a large amount of artefacts and photographs. Fairchild Argus II G-AJOZ is held as a potential future exhibit, but is not available for inspection.

Nearby:

Battle of Britain Memorial Flight Visitor Centre, *2 miles – see page 46.*
Boston, *12 miles.*
City of Lincoln, *20 miles.*
Cranwell Visitor Centre, *15 miles – see page 52.*
Dambusters Heritage Centre, *20 miles – see page 52.*
Lincolnshire Aviation Heritage Centre, *8 miles – see page 52.*
Metheringham Visitor Centre, *10 miles – see page 52.*
Navenby Heritage Room, *16 miles – see page 52.*
Wellingore Heritage Room, *16 miles – see page 52.*

The varied displays at Thorpe Camp are contained in a piece of history – the buildings were the former No.1 Communal Site for the famed Woodhall Spa airfield. Ken Ellis

ALSO IN
THE EAST MIDLANDS

The **LIGHTNING ASSOCIATION** are based on the former RAF Binbrook airfield and they maintain F.6 XR724 in near airworthy condition. They stage an annual 'Lightning Rally' at the airfield to unite all Lightning lovers and publish an excellent house journal. SAE for details to Lightning Association, Binbrook Airfield, Lincolnshire, LN3 6HF.

ROLLS-ROYCE HERITAGE TRUST, Coventry Branch. The closure of the Rolls-Royce factory at Parkside in Coventry in 1994 meant that the excellent collection of aero engines, cars and much else restored and kept by the branch had to relocate to Mickleover, Derbyshire, to premises within the Rolls-Royce Training Centre. There is an annual open day but visits are welcomed at other times by prior arrangement. Send SAE to Rolls-Royce Heritage Trust (Coventry), Ansty, Coventry, CV7 9JR.

Rolls-Royce Heritage Trust Coventry Branch is custodian to a large aero engine collection. Ken Ellis

Note:

The **EAST MIDLANDS AEROPARK & VISITORS CENTRE,** and the associated aircraft collection, at East Midlands Airport, Castle Donington, closed to the public in 1996. There are no immediate plans for it to re-open.

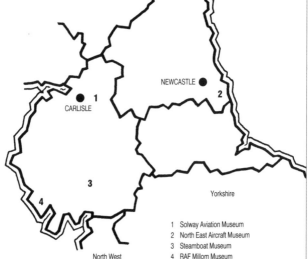

NORTHUMBRIA AND CUMBRIA
Cumbria, Durham, Northumberland and Tyneside

Scotland

NEWCASTLE ●

CARLISLE ● 1

2

Yorkshire

3

4

North West

1 Solway Aviation Museum
2 North East Aircraft Museum
3 Steamboat Museum
4 RAF Millom Museum

Cumbria Tourist Board
Ashleigh, Holly Road, Windermere, Cumbria, LA23 2AQ
Tel: 015394 44444 Fax: 015394 44041

Northumbria Tourist Board
Aykley Heads, Durham, County Durham, DH2 5UX
Tel: 0191 384 0899 Fax: 0191 386 0899

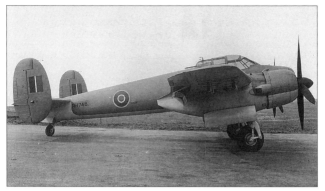

Within the North East Aircraft Museum can be found some unique treasures, including the fuselage of the last Bristol Brigand, RH746, pictured above in 1946 prior to service issue. Ken Ellis collection

NORTH EAST AIRCRAFT MUSEUM
Sunderland, Northumberland

Address: Old Washington Road, Sunderland, SR5 3HZ.
Telephone: 0191 5190662.
Where: N of the A123, off the A1290 Washington Road, follow signs for the Nissan plant.
Open: Every day 10am to 5pm (or dusk in winter).
By rail: Sunderland, 3 miles.
Tourist: Sunderland 0191 5650960 or 0191 5650990, Fax: 0191 5653352.
Admission: Adult £2.00, OAP/child £1.00.
Facilities: Toilets/Parking/Cafe*/Shop/Disabled*/All/Changes.

A new hangar extension housing the shop with visitor and display facilities will open during 1998. Improvements for disabled visitor access are continuing with evening group visits during June to September by prior arrangement. A large and impressive collection of aircraft, with two display halls and a workshop. Themes include NATO com-

bat aircraft, the Royal Observer Corps and search and rescue. The story of aviation in the north east of England is also given good treatment. The museum has a vigorous restoration programme and visitors can keep an eye on the progress of airframes in the workshop.

Aircraft exhibits:

☐	'G-ADVU'*	Mignet HM.14 Flying Flea (BAPC.211)	Fr '36
☐	'G-AFUG'	Luton LA-4 Minor (BAPC.97)	§ '37
☐	G-APTW	Westland Widgeon 2	'59
☐	G-ARHX	DH Dove 8	'61
☐	G-AWRS	Avro Anson C.19	§ '46
☐	G-BEEX	DH Comet 4C nose	'61
☐	G-MBDL	AES Lone Ranger microlight	§ '81
☐	G-OGIL	Short SD.330-100	'81
☐	'G-BAGJ'	Westland Gazelle 1 (G-SFTA)	§ Fr '72
☐	'K-158'	Austin Whippet repro (BAPC.207)	'99
☐	RH746	Bristol Brigand TF.1	§ '46
☐	VV217	DH Vampire FB.5	§ '48
☐	WA577	Bristol Sycamore 3	'49
☐	WB685	DHC Chipmunk T.10 fuselage	Can '50
☐	WD790	Gloster Meteor NF.11 nose	'52

☐ WD889	Fairey Firefly AS.5 cockpit	'53
☐ WG724	Westland Dragonfly HR.5	US '52
☐ WJ639	EE Canberra TT.18	'54
☐ WK198	V-S Swift F.4 fuselage	§ '53
☐ WL181	Gloster Meteor F.8 [X]	'54
☐ WN516	BP Balliol T.2 cockpit	§ '54
☐ WZ518	DH Vampire T.11	'53
☐ WZ767	Slingsby Grasshopper TX.1	'55
☐ XG680	DH Sea Venom FAW.22 [438]	'57
☐ XL319	Avro Vulcan B.2	'61
☐ XN258	Westland Whirlwind HAR.9 [589-CU]	US '59
☐ XP627	Hunting Jet Provost T.4	'62
☐ XT236	Bell Sioux AH.1 (Westland)	§ US '66
☐ XW276	Westland Gazelle 03	Fr '70
☐ ZF594	EE Lightning F.53	'68
☐ A-522	FMA Pucara	Arg c76
☐ E-419	Hawker Hunter F.51	'56
☐ 146	Dassault Mystère IVA [8-MG]	Fr '55

☐ 6171	NA F-86D-35-NA Sabre	US '51
☐ 26541	Republic F-84F Thunderstreak	US '52
☐ 42157	NA F-100D Super Sabre [11-ML]	US '54
☐ 54439	Lockheed T-33A T-Bird [WI]	US '54
☐ –	Bensen B.7 gyroglider (BAPC.119)	US c67
☐ –	Brown Helicopter (BAPC.96)	§ '62
☐ –	Chargus Olympus hang glider (BAPC.228)	§ c81
☐ –	HP C-10A Jetstream cockpit (mock-up)	'69

Nearby:

Beamish North of England Open Air Museum, *10 miles.*

Maritime Museum, Hartlepool, *20 miles.*

City of Newcastle upon Tyne, *8 miles.*

Ryhope Engines Museum, *7 miles.*

City of Sunderland, *3 miles.*

RAF MILLOM MUSEUM

Haverigg, Cumbria

Address: South Copeland Aviation Group, c/o John Nixon, RAF Millom Museum Project, HM Prison Haverigg, Millom, Cumbria, LA18 4NA.

Where: On the Bankhead Estate, North Lane, Haverigg, adjacent to HMP Haverigg.

Open: Open Saturdays and Sunday 10am to 5pm Easter to end of November. Summer months additionally Monday, Wednesday and Friday 10am to 5pm. Other times by arrangement.

By bus: Services from Millom.

By rail: Millom 2 miles.

Tourist: Barrow-in-Furness 01229 870156, Fax: 01229 432289.

Admission: Adult £1.00, children 20p.

Facilities: Toilets/Parking/Kids/All/Changes.

A small museum housed in buildings that were previously part of the former RAF Millom airfield – now largely occupied by HMP Haverigg. Within the prison is a thriving restoration workshop, with the Flying Flea and Vampire 'pod' being shining examples of their workmanship. Displays chart the history of the airfield and of military aviation in the region, including the many crashes in local waters and on the surrounding hills.

Aircraft exhibits:

☐ 'G-ADRX'	Mignet HM.14 Flying Flea (BAPC.231)	§ Fr c36
☐ WD377	DHC Chipmunk T.10 cockpit	'51
☐ WP255	DH Vampire NF.10 cockpit	'51
☐ XK637	DH Vampire T.11	'56
☐ XM660	Westland Whirlwind HAS.7	US '58
☐ XD425	Vampire T.11 nose [16]	§ '54

Nearby:

The Lake District, *18 miles.*

Ravenglass and Eskdale Miniature Railway, *16 miles.*

Sellafield Visitor Centre, *18 miles.*

Steamboat Museum, *18 miles* – see page 64.

SOLWAY AVIATION MUSEUM

Carlisle Airport, Cumbria

Address: 'Aviation House', Carlisle Airport, Crosby-on-Eden, Carlisle, Cumbria, CA6 4NW.

Where: Carlisle Airport, on the B6264 east of Carlisle and signposted.

Open: Sundays 11am to 5pm. Other times by prior arrangement.

By rail: Carlisle, 6 miles.

Tourist: Carlisle 01228 512444, Fax: 01228 511758.

Admission: £2.50, child £1.25, family £6.00.

Facilities: Parking/Shop/Disabled/All/Changes/X. (Toilets and cafe within the airport terminal.)

In May 1996 the Solway Aviation Society (SAS) opened up the first phase of their newly-refurbished display building, to great acclaim by visitors. The museum is set within a large airfield building and the first sections are devoted to life in the area in the 1940s and 1950s. A 'Spadeadam room' includes material collected from the former rocket test site, including Blue Streak hardware. Local aviation and airfields are heavily represented and visitors can catch a glimpse of restoration work on the Auster. At the aircraft park, the Vulcan cockpit is open for inspection during weekends.

Aircraft exhibits:

☐ G-APLG	Auster J/5L Aiglet Trainer		'58
☐ G-AYFA	SAL Twin Pioneer 3 nose		'58
☐ WE188	EE Canberra T.4		'52
☐ WS832	Gloster Meteor NF.14 [W]		'54
☐ WV198	Westland Whirlwind HAR.21		
	(G-BJWY) [K]		US '52
☐ WZ515	DH Vampire T.11		'53
☐ XJ823	Avro Vulcan B.2		'61
☐ ZF583	EE Lightning F.53		'68

Nearby:

City of Carlisle, *6 miles.*

Hadrian's Wall and Roman Forts, *12 and 20 miles.*

An element of the engine display hall at the Solway Aviation Museum. Ken Ellis

STEAMBOAT MUSEUM
Windermere, Cumbria

Address: Rayrigg Road, Windermere, Cumbria, LA23 1BN.

Telephone: 01539 445565.
Web-site: http://www.steamboat.co.uk

Where: Signposted within the town, on the lakefront.

Open: Open Easter to Oct, daily 10am to 5pm.

By bus: Several bus services into Windermere.

By rail: Windermere, 1 mile.

Tourist: Windermere 01539 446499, Fax: 01539 448769.

Admission: Adult £3.00, child £2.00, family £8.00.

Facilities: Toilets/Parking/Shop/Disabled*/All/ Changes.

Within the collection of unique Victorian and Edwardian steam launches, many of which still cruise the lake can be found the equally unique waterglider, which was converted in 1943 to flying-boat guise for trials. Along with the waterglider is a display showing aviation on and around the lake since 1911.

Aircraft exhibit:

☐ BGA.266 Slingsby T.1 Falcon waterglider '36

Nearby:
The Lake District and its many attractions –
Ambleside, *6 miles;* Lakeside to Haverthwaite Railway, *6 miles;* Coniston, *8 miles.*
Kendal, *8 miles.*
Keswick, *20 miles.*
RAF Millom Museum, *18 miles – see page 62.*

A conversion of a standard Slingsby Falcon, the waterglider was the brainchild of T C Pattinson and it first flew in 1943. It was hoped that it would lead to water-launching troop-carrying gliders for use in the liberation of Europe. Ken Ellis

NORTH WEST ENGLAND
Cheshire, Greater Manchester, Lancashire, Merseyside

1   Museum of Science & Industry
    Manchester
2   Warship Preservation Trust
3   Griffin Trust

North West Tourist Board
Swan House, Swan Meadow Road, Wigan Pier, Wigan, WN3 5BB
Tel: 01942 821222 Fax: 01942 820002

GRIFFIN TRUST
Hooton Park, South Wirral

Address: Hooton Park, North Road, Ellesmere
Port, South Wirral, Merseyside, L65 1BQ.
Telephone: 0151 350 2598.
Where: South of Junction 6 of the M53, near
Eastham Locks. Follow Hooton Park signs.
Open: Sundays 10am to 3pm. Otherwise by prior
arrangement.
Tourist: Chester 01244 351609. Fax: 01244
400420.
Admission: Adult £2.50, concessions £1.50.
Facilities: Toilets/Parking/Cafe/All.

Work continues to establish the site as a centre of
transport and technological heritage. Located
within 'Belfast Truss' hangars of the former Hooton
Park aerodrome, the site is largely occupied now
by Vauxhall Motors, whose badge has inspired the
naming of the Trust. Special events are occasionally held.

Aircraft exhibit:

| ☐ WF911 | EE Canberra B.2 nose | '53 |

Nearby:
City of Chester, 9 miles.
City of Liverpool, 10 miles (via tunnel)
Ellesmere Port Boat Museum, 3 miles.
Warship Preservation Trust, Birkenhead, 7 miles –
see page 68.

MUSEUM OF SCIENCE AND INDUSTRY AIR & SPACE GALLERY
Manchester, Greater Manchester

Address: Liverpool Road, Castlefield,
Manchester, M3 4JP.
Telephone: 0161 832 2244
or 24-hour information line 0161 832 1830,
Fax: 0161 833 2184.
Where: Close to the end of the A57 in central
Manchester, well signposted.
Open: Every day from 10am to 5pm, including
Bank Holidays but excluding December 23-25.
By bus: Metrolink tram stop nearby. No 33 from
Piccadilly Gardens stops outside.
By rail: Deansgate, walking distance.
Tourist: Manchester 0161 2343157 or
0161 2343158, Fax: 0161 2369900.
Admission: Adult £5, Child/cons £3.
Facilities: Toilets/Parking/Cafe/Shop/Disabled/
All/Changes/Brochure.

The air and space gallery of the Museum of Science and Industry is just the tip of the iceberg in
this amazing seven acre site. The aviation hall
includes a gallery that offers interesting aspects
and angles on the airframes. The Trident cockpit
offers a close view of the world inside an airliner,
the Super-X simulator can take all-comers for the
nearest thing to a real flight and the space gallery
includes interactive displays. The remainder of the
museum has to be seen as well, including the
Power Hall with working steam and other engines,
the world's oldest surviving passenger railway station (Liverpool Road) complete with a variety of
rolling stock and locomotives, underground Manchester – take a walk through a sewer – and much
more.

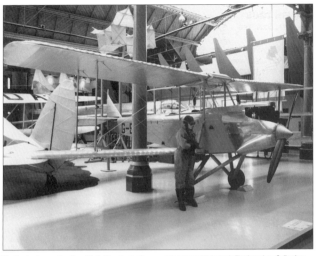

Working in close conjunction with the Manchester Museum of Science and Industry is The Aeroplane Collection. Among their aircraft on display is Avro Avian G-EBZM. Ken Ellis

Aircraft exhibits:

☐ G-EBZM	Avro Avian IIIA	'28
☐ G-ABAA	Avro 504K	'30
☐ G-ADAH	DH Dragon Rapide	§ '35
☐ G-AJEB	Auster J/1N Alpha	'47
☐ G-APUD	Bensen B.7M	US '59
☐ G-AWZP	HS Trident 3B-101 nose	'72
☐ G-AYTA	MS Rallye Club	§ '71
☐ MT847	V-S Spitfire XIV [AX-H]	'45
☐ WG763	EE P.1A	'55
☐ WP270	Slingsby Eton TX.1	§ '55
☐ WR960	Avro Shackleton AEW.2	'54
☐ WT619	Hawker Hunter F.1	'54
☐ WZ736	Avro 707A	'53
☐ XG454	Bristol Belvedere HC.1	'62
☐ XL824	Bristol Sycamore HR.14	'57
☐ 997	Yokosuka MXY-7 Ohka 11 suicide weapon	Ja '45

☐ –	Cayley Glider replica (BAPC.89)	1853
☐ –	Flexiform hang-glider (BAPC.252)	§ c82
☐ –	Hiway Spectrum hang-glider (BAPC.259)	§ c80
☐ –	Mignet HM.14 Flying Flea (BAPC.12)	Fr '36
☐ –	Roe Triplane replica (BAPC.6) [14]	'09
☐ –	Volmer VJ-23 Swingwing microlight (BAPC.175)	US '78
☐ –	Wood Ornithopter (BAPC.182)	§ c65

Nearby:
East Lancashire Railway, *10 miles.*
Granada Studios Experience, *adjacent.*
Manchester Airport Viewing Park, *8 miles.*
Manchester City Centre *walking distance.*
Manchester Transport Museum, *2 miles.*
Quarry Bank Mill, *10 miles.*

WARSHIP PRESERVATION TRUST

Birkenhead Docks, Merseyside

Address: Warship Preservation Trust, Birkenhead, L41 1DJ.
Telephone: 0151 650 1573, plus Fax.
Where: Birkenhead Docks, signposted.
Open: Open daily from 10am to 5pm.
By bus: Several services pass close by.
By rail: Birkenhead, 1 mile.
Tourist: Birkenhead 0151 6476780.
Admission: TBA.
Facilities: Toilets/Parking/Cafe/Shop/All.

HMS *Plymouth* has been berthed in Birkenhead since 1991 and has proved to be a popular attraction, including the Wasp helicopter in the hangar. Also on public view is the submarine HMS *Onyx*. During summer weekends and school holidays the Liverpool Bar Lightship is also available for inspection. along with a D-Day landing craft.

Aircraft exhibit:

☐ XS570　Westland Wasp HAS.1 [445]　'65

Nearby:
Boat Museum, Ellesmere Port, *10 miles.*
City of Chester, *14 miles.*
City of Liverpool, *3 miles.*
Griffin Trust, Hooton Park, *8 miles – see page 66.*
Mersey Ferries, *1 mile.*
Mouldsworth Motor Museum, *18 miles.*

ALSO IN THE NORTH WEST

At **BARTON AERODROME** (on the A57 west of Manchester) is a Visitor Centre with a small collection of airframes (including an EE Canberra T.4 nose). The car park offers good views of the activity at the aerodrome.

The amazing antiques and craft centre **BOTANY BAY VILLAGE** at Chorley, Lancs, includes a growing collection of airframes: BAC 111-320 5N-AOK, Bristol Sycamore HR.14 XG540, DH Venom cockpit, Hunting Jet Provost T.4 XP688 and Westland Whirlwind HAS.7 XN385 as attractions. Open daily. (Tel: 01257 261220.)

Inside the Botany Bay Village Craft Centre – a former Swiss Air Force Venom cockpit amongst the antiques.
Alan Curry

SOUTH EAST ENGLAND

Kent, Surrey, East Sussex, West Sussex

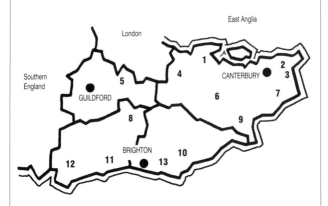

1 Royal Engineers Museum	5 Brooklands Museum	10 Foulkes-Halbard Collection
2 Hurricane & Spitfire Memorial Building	6 Lashenden Air Warfare Museum	11 Museum of D-Day Aviation
3 Manston Historical Society Museum	7 Kent Battle of Britain Museum	12 Tangmere Military Aviation Museum
4 Shoreham Aircraft Museum	8 Skyview Visitors Centre, Gatwick	13 Newhaven Fort
	9 Brenzett Aeronautical Museum	

South East Tourist Board
The Old Brew House, Warwick Park, Tunbridge Wells, Kent, TN2 5TU
Tel: 01892 540766 Fax: 01892 511008

BRENZETT AERONAUTICAL MUSEUM

Brenzett, Kent

Address: Ivychurch Road, Brenzett, Romney Marsh, Kent TN29 0EE.

Telephone: 01233 627911.

Where: Brenzett in on the A259 north west of New Romney. The museum is on an unclasssified road to Ivychurch.

Open: Sundays and Bank Holidays from Easter to end of October, 11am to 5.30pm and Tuesdays, Wednesdays and Thursdays, July to end of October from 2pm to 5.30pm.

By rail: Rye 7 miles.

Tourist: Rye 01797 226696.

Admission: Adult £1.75, OAP £1, Child 50p.

Facilities: Toilets/Parking/Shop/All/Changes/Brochure/X.

Using buildings occupied by the Women's Land Army (WLA) during the Second World War, the museum overlooks the former Advanced Landing Ground (ALG) that carried the names of Brenzett or Ivychurch and was used briefly during the run-up to D-Day and beyond. There is a small static park of aircraft and large artefacts and an impressive memorial to those who worked and fought from all of Kent's ALGs. The museum contains a wealth of material on Brenzett, military aviation in Kent and includes a display on life in the WLA.

Aircraft exhibits:

☐ G-AMSM	Douglas Dakota 4 nose	US '43
☐ V7350	Hawker Hurricane I wreck	'40
☐ WH657	EE Canberra B.2	'52
☐ XK625	DH Vampire T.11 nose [12]	'56

Nearby:

Folkestone and Hastings, *16 miles.*
Kent and East Sussex Railway, *9 miles.*
Kent Battle of Britain Museum, *16 miles.*
Lashenden Air Warfare Museum, *14 miles – see page 75.*
Romney, Hythe & Dymchurch Railway, *12 miles.*

Below: **One of the display halls at Brenzett.** Ken Ellis

The famed clubhouse at Brooklands was used postwar as a design office by Barnes Wallis. The rich mixture of classic cars and aircraft is apparent throughout the museum. Brooklands Museum

BROOKLANDS MUSEUM
Weybridge, Surrey

Address: The Clubhouse, Brooklands Road, Weybridge, Surrey, KT13 0QN.

Telephone: 01932 857381, Fax: 01932 855465.

Where: On the B374 south of Weybridge, access from Junctions 10 or 12 of the M25.

Open: Tuesday to Sunday and Bank Holidays 10am to 5pm (last entry 4pm), Easter to October. Winter months, 10am to 4pm, last entry is 3pm. Note: *closed* on Mondays. Normally closed Good Friday and Xmas. Pre-arranged guided tours available Tuesdays to Fridays, by telephoning the museum.

By bus: Local services out of Weybridge.

By rail: Weybridge 2 miles.

Tourist: Twickenham 0181 8911411.

Admission: Adult £4.50, Cons/Child £2.50, Family ticket £12.50.

Facilities: Toilets/Parking/Cafe/Shop/Disabled/All/Changes/Brochure.

Brooklands has always been a heady combination of aviation and motor racing and so it remains. On the aeronautical side there is Barnes Wallis' stratosphere test chamber and the balloon hangar, the world's first flight ticket office, the reconstruction of A V Roe's 1908 aircraft shed and the finishing straight hangar which houses, amongst others, the famed Loch Ness Wellington 'R-Robert'. On the motor racing side there is the clubhouse, Malcolm Campbell's workshop, the car collection, the hill climb, and the banked circuit. There are many special events, both wheel and wing-borne and a variety of exhibitions staged each year.

Aircraft exhibits:

☐ A40-AB	BAC VC-10 1103		'64
☐ F-BGEQ	DH Tiger Moth		'43
☐ 'G-EBED'	Vickers Viking repro		'19
☐ 'G-AACA'	Avro 504K repro	§	'18
☐ 'G-ADRY'	Mignet HM.14 Flying Flea	Fr	c37
☐ G-AEKV	Kronfeld Drone de Luxe		'36
☐ G-AGRU	Vickers Viking 1		'46
☐ G-APEJ	Vickers Vanguard 953C nose		'61

☐ G-APEP	Vickers Vanguard 953C	'62
☐ G-APIM	Vickers Viscount 806	'58
☐ G-ASYD	BAC 111-475AM	'65
☐ G-BJHV	Voisin scale repro	Fr '07
☐ G-LOTI	Blériot XI repro	Fr '09
☐ G-MJPB	Manuel Ladybird microlight	'82
☐ G-VTOL	HS Harrier T.52	'71
☐ 'B7270'	Sopwith Camel repro ✈ (G-BFCZ)	'18
☐ 'F5475'	RAF SE.5A repro (BAPC.250)	'18
☐ 'K5673'	Hawker Fury II repro (BAPC.249)	'31
☐ N2980	Vickers Wellington IA	'39
☐ WF372	Vickers Varsity T.1 [A]	'51
☐ WP921	DHC Chipmunk T.10 cockpit	'52
☐ WT859	V-S 544 nose	'56
☐ XD816	Vickers Valiant BK.1 nose	'56
☐ XJ571	DH Sea Vixen FAW.2	'58
☐ XL621	Hawker Hunter T.7	'59
☐ XT575	Vickers Viscount 837 nose	'60
☐ Z2389	Hawker Hurricane IIa	'40
☐ E-421	Hawker Hunter F.51	'56
☐ 'U-1215'	DH Vampire T.11 (XE998)	'55
☐ –	Abbott-Baynes Scud I repro (HFZ)	'34
☐ –	Abbott-Baynes Scud II (AAA)	'35

☐ –	BAC/SNIAS Concorde nose	c70
☐ –	BAC TSR-2 nose	'64
☐ –	BAC VC-10 nose	c62
☐ –	Hols der Teufel glider repro ✈ (FHQ)	Gr c33
☐ –	Manuel Willow Wren ((BGA.162)	'34
☐ –	Roe I Biplane repro (BAPC.187)	'08
☐ –	Rogallo hang glider	US c76
☐ –	Santos-Dumont Demoiselle repro (BAPC.194)	'11
☐ –	Santos-Dumont Demoiselle repro (BAPC.256)	'11
☐ –	Slingsby Gull III glider ✈ (ATH)	'45
☐ –	Vickers Vimy cockpit repro	'18

Nearby:

Airborne Forces Museum, *16 mls – see page 82.*
Central London, *16 miles.*
Imperial War Museum, *16 miles – see page 38.*
Royal Air Force Museum, *20 miles – see page 40.*
Science Museum, *16 miles – see page 43.*
Windsor Castle and Safari Park, *10 miles.*

FOULKES-HALBARD COLLECTION

Wannock, East Sussex

Address: Filching Manor, Jevington Road, Wannock, Polegate, East Sussex, BN26 5QA.

Telephone: 01323 487838 or 01323 487124, Fax: 01323 486331.

Where: On the road to Jevington from Wannock, East Sussex. Signposted from the A22.

Open: Daily Easter to May Thursday to Sunday; May to October daily, 10.30am to 4.30pm. Other times by appointment.

By bus: Services from Eastbourne stop in Wannock.

By rail: Polegate 2 miles.

Tourist: Eastbourne 01323 411400, Fax: 01323 649574.

Admission: £3 adult, Child/cons £2.

Facilities: Toilets/Parking/Cafe/Shop/Disabled/ Kids/All/Changes/Brochure.

There are many items at this venue queuing up for the accolade of 'star' not the least of which is the manor house itself which dates back to the 15th century. Aeronautically, the collection contains two aircraft – with the owner looking for more suitable examples – the Aldritt monoplane, a pioneer from Ireland, and the Jupiter man-powered aircraft. Other items include a Rolls-Royce 'R' engine from the 1931 Schneider Trophy winning Supermarine team and a 1947 MetroVick Beryl. The car collection here is superb ranging from the 1898 Orient Express to the 1997 Arrows driven by Damon Hill. Also here is the original Campbell Bluebird K3 hydroplane record breaker of Sir Malcolm Campbell and a reproduction of the Bluebird K7 of

Donald Campbell. Special events are frequently staged including go-cart racing on the Campbell Circuit.

Aircraft exhibits:

☐ –	Aldritt Monoplane (IAHC.2)		§ '10
☐ –	Halton Jupiter man-powered aircraft (BAPC.127)		'72

Nearby:
Bluebell Railway, *16 miles.*
Eastbourne, *4 miles.*
English Wine Centre, *2 miles.*
Hastings, *17 miles.*
Newhaven Fort, *8 miles – see page 77.*
Museum of D-Day Aviation and Shoreham Aerodrome, *20 miles – see page 76.*

HURRICANE & SPITFIRE MEMORIAL BUILDING
RAF Manston, Kent

Address: RAF Manston, Ramsgate, Kent, CT12 5BS.
Telephone: 08143 823351, ext 2219.
Where: RAF Manston, follow the signs off the A253 Ramsgate road.
Open: Daily, May to September 10am to 5pm, October to April 10am to 4pm.
By bus: Services to Ramsgate and Margate, 3 miles.
By rail: Ramsgate 3 miles.
Tourist: Ramsgate 01843 591086.
Admission: Free. Donation much appreciated.
Facilities: Toilets/Parking/Cafe/Shop/Disabled/All/Changes/Brochure.

Within the building can be found two pristine examples of the immortal Hurricane and Spitfire – both restored by the Medway Aircraft Preservation Society (see page 80). Also within is a wealth of material relating to Manston's role in the Battle of Britain and throughout the Second World War.

Aircraft exhibits:

☐ 'BN230'	Hawker Hurricane II (LF751) [FT-A]		'44
☐ TB752	V-S Spitfire XVI [KH-Z]		'45

Nearby:
Canterbury, *12 miles.*
Kent Battle of Britain Museum, *18 miles – see below.*
Manston Historical Society Museum – adjacent, *see page 75.*
Maritime Museum & Motor Museum, Ramsgate, *3 miles.*

KENT BATTLE OF BRITAIN MUSEUM
Hawkinge, Kent

Address: Aerodrome Road, Hawkinge Airfield, Folkestone, CT18 7AG.
Telephone: 01303 893140.
Where: Signposted off the A260 at Hawkinge, north of Folkestone.
Open: Daily Easter to end of September 10am to 5pm and October 11am to 4pm.
By bus: No 16 from Folkestone stops at entrance.

By rail: Folkestone 3 miles.
Tourist: Folkestone 01303 258594, Fax: 01303 259754.
Admission: Adult £3.00, OAP £2.5, Child £1.50.
Facilities: Toilets/Parking/Cafe*/Shop/Disabled*/All/Changes/Brochure.

Within the museum is a renowned collection of artefacts charting every aspect of the Battle of Britain in Kent. A series of reproduction aircraft have been used to recreate scenarios and the majority of the items on show come from crash sites in the area. Presently, items on show come from nearly 600 Battle of Britain aircraft. Displays take in uniforms, awards, airfield histories, weapons and much more. The original Operations Block, from which all air operations at Hawkinge were controlled during the Battle of Britain and the airfield armoury house exhibits, adding further to the heady atmosphere of this museum.

Aircraft exhibits:

☐ 'D-3-340'	Grunau Baby 2 glider	Gr c36
☐ 'K5054'	V-S Spitfire prototype FSM	'36
☐ 'N3289'	V-S Spitfire (BAPC.65) [DW-K]	'39
☐ 'N3313'	V-S Spitfire (BAPC.69) [KL-B]	§ '39
☐ 'P3059'	Hawker Hurricane replica (BAPC.64) [SD-N]	'40
☐ 'P3208'	Hawker Hurricane FSM (BAPC.63) [SD-T]	'40
☐ 'MK356'	V-S Spitfire IX	'41
☐ –	Hawker Hurricane FSM	'40
☐ –	Fieseler Fi 103 (V-1) flying-bomb replica (BAPC.36)	Gr '45
☐ –	Messerschmitt Bf 109 replica (BAPC.66)	§ Gr '40
☐ –	Messerschmitt Bf 109 replica (BAPC.67)	Gr '40
☐ –	Messerschmitt Bf 109 replica (BAPC.74)	Gr '40

Nearby:

Battle of Britain Memorial, *3 miles.*
Brenzett Aeronautical Museum, *16 miles – see page 70.*
Dover, *6 miles.*
Eurotunnel Exhibition, *5 miles.*
Folkestone, *3 miles.*
Hurricane and Spitfire Memorial Building, *18 miles – see page 73.*
Manston Historical Society Museum, *18 miles – see page 75.*
Romney, Hythe & Dymchurch Railway, *10 miles.*

Within the specially-constructed Stuart-Buttle hangar are reproduction Hurricane and Spitfires used in the epic 1968 film *The Battle of Britain* plus vehicles and large artefacts. Ken Ellis

LASHENDEN AIR WARFARE MUSEUM

Headcorn Aerodrome, Kent

Address: Lashenden Aerodrome, Ashford, Kent, TN27 9HX.
Telephone: 01622 890226, Fax: 01622 890876.
Where: Lashenden (or Headcorn) aerodrome, off the A274 south of Headcorn.
Open: Sundays and Bank Holidays 10.30am to 6pm from Easter until the end of October. Parties at other times by prior arrangement.
By bus: No 12 passes close to the museum.
By rail: Headcorn 2 miles.
Tourist: Ashford 01233 629165.
Admission: Free, donations welcomed.
Facilities: Toilets/Parking/Cafe/Shop/Changes/Brochure/X.

Lashenden served as an Advanced Landing Ground during the run-up to D-Day and the museum concentrates on the airfield's role. The airfield today is a thriving general aviation and parachute centre and activity can be seen from the museum enclosure to advantage. The small static aircraft park is supported by a huge array of artefacts, all carefully labelled and telling the tale of military aviation in Kent and life in wartime.

Aircraft exhibits:

☐ WZ450	DH Vampire T.11 nose [19]		'52
☐ WZ589	DH Vampire T.11 [19]		'53
☐ XN380	Westland Whirlwind HAS.7 [67]	US '61	
☐ 84	Dassault Mystère IVA [8-NF]	Fr '55	
☐ 63938	NA F-100F Super Sabre [11-MU]	US '56	
☐ 100549	Focke-Achgelis Fa 330A-1 rotorkite	Gr '44	
☐ –	Fieseler Fi 103R-IV piloted flying-bomb (BAPC 91)	Gr '45	

Nearby:
Brenzett Aeronautical Museum, *14 miles –* see page 70.
Hastings, *20 miles.*
Kent and East Sussex Railway, *8 miles.*
Romney, Hythe & Dymchurch Railway, *20 miles.*
Royal Engineers Museum, *16 miles –* see page 77.

MANSTON HISTORICAL SOCIETY MUSEUM

Address: RAF Manston, Ramsgate, Kent, CT12 5BS.
Telephone: 01843 823351.
Where: At RAF Manston, follow the signs off the A253 Ramsgate road.
Open: Monday to Saturday 1pm to 5pm, Sunday and Bank Holidays 10am to 5pm.
By bus: From Ramsgate and Margate, 3 miles.
By rail: Ramsgate, 3 miles
Tourist: Ramsgate 01843 591086
Admission: Free, donations welcomed.
Facilities: Toilets/Parking/Disabled*/All/Changes/Brochure. Cafe at the Hurricane and Spitfire building, adjacent, see page 75.

Opened for the first time to the public during Easter 1998, the museum harnesses a wealth of history at Manston itself and in the area. Major exhibits include a Battle of Britain 'ops' room and a 'Cold War' fighter control room.

Aircraft exhibits:

☐ EJ922	Hawker Typhoon Ib cockpit	'43
☐ WB584	DHC Chipmunk T.10 cockpit	'50
☐ WD646	Gloster Meteor TT.20	'51
☐ –	Hawker Typhoon I cockpit	c43
☐ –	RAF BE.2c repro (BAPC.117)	'16

Nearby:
Canterbury, *12 miles.*
Hurricane & Spitfire Memorial Building, *adjacent –* see page 73.
Kent Battle of Britain Museum, *18 miles –* see page 73.

MUSEUM OF D-DAY AVIATION
Shoreham Airport, West Sussex

Address: Shoreham Aerodrome, Shoreham-by-Sea, West Sussex, BN43 5FJ.

Telephone: 01374 971971.

Where: Shoreham Airport, access off the A27 east of Worthing.

Open: 11am to 5pm daily March to November.

By bus: Regular services into Shoreham-by-Sea.

By rail: Shoreham 1 mile.

Tourist: Worthing 01903 210022.

Admission: Adult £2.50, OAP £2, Child £1.50, Family £5.

Facilities: Toilets/Parking/Cafe/Shop/Disabled/All/Changes/Brochure.

Shoreham harbour played a pivotal role during the D-Day operation and of course the entire south coast was deeply involved in one form or another. The museum serves to outline the effects of the aerial armada on the region, its preparation, execution and aftermath. A vast collection of artefacts, including a growing collection of military fire engines and an RAF air sea rescue boat. The museum offers excellent views of the comings and goings of aircraft from delightful Shoreham aerodrome. Special events, reunions and exhibitions are frequently staged, including an annual fire engine rally.

Aircraft exhibit:

☐	'MJ751'	Sup Spitfire replica (BAPC.209)	[DU-V]	'44
☐	XS932	EE Lightning F.6 nose		'67

Also:

Excellent cafe and viewing facilities within the terminal building, including a terraced area under the control tower. Within the terminal can be found small displays showing the history of the aerodrome.

Nearby:

Bluebell Railway, *18 miles.*

Brighton, *6 miles.*

The Lavender Line, *18 miles.*

Newhaven Fort, *16 miles – see opposite.*

Skyview Visitors Centre, Gatwick Airport, *20 miles – see page 78.*

Tangmere Military Aviation Museum, *20 miles – see page 79.*

A largely original forward fuselage of an Airspeed Horsa assault glider is one of the many exhibits at the Museum of D-Day Aviation at Shoreham. Ken Ellis

NEWHAVEN FORT

Newhaven, East Sussex

Address: Fort Road, Newhaven, East Sussex, BN9 9DL. **Telephone:** 01273 517622.

Where: Close to the mouth of the River Ouse, signposted in the town.

Open: 1st April to 1st October, daily 10.30am to 6.00pm. Also weekends in March and October and School Half Terms.

By bus: On the main bus route in the town.

By rail: Newhaven 1 mile.

Tourist: Seaford 01323 897426.

Admission: Adult £3.60, OAP £2.95, Child £1.95.

Facilities: Toilets/Parking/Cafe/Shop/Disabled*/ Kids/All/Changes/Brochure.

Set in 10 acres of 1860s coastal defence fort, with underground tunnels and bunkers to explore. Excellent views of the coast and the ferries. Displays on the Dieppe raid, the Royal Observer Corps, the Home front, D-Day and much more. A display by the Robertsbridge Aviation Society – see page 80 – includes a Meteor nose section

Aircraft exhibit:

☐ WA630	Gloster Meteor T.7 nose	'50

Nearby:

Bluebell Railway, *12 miles*.

Brighton, *12 miles*.

Eastbourne, *10 miles*.

Foulkes-Halbard Collection, *8 miles – page 72*.

The Lavender Line, *10 miles*.

ROYAL ENGINEERS MUSEUM

Gillingham, Kent

Address: Prince Arthur Road, Gillingham, Kent, ME4 4UG.

Telephone: 01634 406397, Fax: 01634 822371.

Where: On the B2007 off the A231 Chatham to Gillingham road. Signposted.

Open: Open Monday to Thursday 10am to 5pm, Saturday, Sunday and Bank Holidays 11.30am to 5pm. Friday by appointment only.

By bus: Several bus services pass nearby.

By rail: Gillingham 1 mile.

Tourist: Rochester 01634 843666.

Admission: Adult £2, Cons £1. Family tickets available.

Facilities: Toilets/Parking/Cafe/Shop/Disabled/ All/Changes/Brochure.

The Royal Engineers were responsible for the development of military aviation in Britain, beginning in 1880 with balloons, then man-lifting kites and airships until the advent of the RFC in 1912. The aviation content of the galleries includes a Harrier in an airfield 'hide'. There is much to interest the aviation enthusiast here including the medals etc of James McCudden VC DSO* MC* MM and many other artefacts. The fascinating world of military engineering through the ages is shown through displays, vehicles and artefacts.

Aircraft exhibits:

☐ XT133	Bell (Agusta) Sioux AH.1	§ US '65
☐ XZ964	HS Harrier GR.3 [D]	'80
☐ –	Military balloon basket	c12
☐ –	Vulcan hang-glider	c80

Nearby:

Chatham Historic Dockyard, *2 miles*.

Fort Amherst, *1 mile*.

Lashenden Air Warfare Museum, *16 miles – see page 75.*

Medway Aircraft Preservation Society, *4 miles – see page 80.*

Shoreham Aircraft Museum,Kent, *18 miles – see page 78*

SHOREHAM AIRCRAFT MUSEUM
Shoreham, Kent

Address: High Street, Shoreham Village, Sevenoaks, Kent, TN14 7TB.
Telephone: 01959 524416.
Where: Off the A225 north of Sevenoaks.
Open: May to September Sundays only 10am to 5pm, or by prior arrangement.
By rail: Shoreham, walking distance.
Tourist: Sevenoaks 01732 450305.
Admission: Adult £1, children free.
Facilities: Toilets/Parking*/Cafe/Shop/Disabled*/All/Changes/Brochure.

A superb museum based upon the society's extensive number of 'digs', all beautifully researched and presented. Large art gallery devoted to the work of local artist Geoff Nutkins.

Aircraft exhibit:

☐ TB885   V-S Spitfire XVI cockpit   § '45

Nearby:
Central London, *16 miles.*
Chatham Historic Dockyard, *16 miles.*
Imperial War Museum, *16 miles – see page 38.*
Museum of Artillery, *16 miles – see page 39.*
RAF Biggin Hill Memorial Chapel, *5 miles.*
Royal Engineers Museum, *18 miles – page 77.*
Science Museum, *16 miles – see page 43.*

SKYVIEW VISITORS CENTRE
Gatwick Airport, West Sussex

Address: Gatwick Airport, West Sussex
Telephone: 01293 502244
Where: South Terminal, Gatwick Airport. Access off the M23, junction 9. Signposted.
Open: TBA.
By bus: Refer to TIC.
By rail: Gatwick Airport station.
Tourist: Gatwick 01293 560108
Admission: TBA.
Facilities: Toilets/Parking/Disabled/All/X.

Located in the South Terminal of Gatwick Airport, the centre offers much more than a distraction for passengers awaiting flights. Located at the northern corner of the terminal there is a spectators gallery offering commanding views of the arrivals and departures. Much of the displays and entertainments are inter-active. The Herald and Comet nose section can be viewed at close quarters.

Aircraft exhibits:

☐ 'G-AMXA'   DH Comet C.2R nose (XK655)   '53
☐ G-CEXP   HP Herald 209   '68

Nearby:
Bluebell Railway, *8 miles.*
Brighton, *20 miles.*
Croydon Airport heritage site, *17 miles – see page 44.*
Museum of D-Day Avn, *20 miles – see page 76.*
Royal Tunbridge Wells and the Spa Valley Railway, *20 miles.*

Visitors can inspect the cockpit of Comet C.2R 'G-AMXA' at Skyview, Gatwick. Andrew Powell

TANGMERE MILITARY AVIATION MUSEUM

Tangmere, West Sussex

Address: Tangmere Airfield, Chichester, West Sussex, PO20 6ES.

Telephone: 01243 775223, Fax: 01243 789490.

Where: Signposted from the A27, nr Chichester.

Open: Daily 10am to 5.30pm March to October; 10am to 4.30pm in February and November.

By bus: Chichester service passes the museum.

By rail: Chichester 3 miles.

Tourist: Chichester 01243 775888, Fax: 01243 539449.

Admission: Adult £3, OAPs £2.50, Child £1.

Facilities: Toilets/Parking/Cafe/Shop/Disabled/ Kids/All/Changes/Brochure.

An excellent museum, situated on the boundary of this former historic airfield. There is an external aircraft display area and four halls within charting 60 years of military aviation in Sussex. The Tangmere Hall concentrates on the history of the airfield from 1917-70. The Middle Hall covers a wide series of subjects, including the 'Dam Busters'. The Battle of Britain Hall contains a huge amount of material on the men and machines of the battle, including a major display on F/L J Nicolson VC. The Merston Hall includes a Hurricane and a Spitfire FSM and the Hunter prototype which achieved record breaking two fame flying from Tangmere. Special exhibitions are frequently staged.

Aircraft exhibits:

☐	'K5054'	V-S Spitfire prototype FSM (BAPC.214)		'36
☐	'L1679'	Hawker Hurricane FSM (BAPC.241) [JX-G]		'38
☐	'BL924'	V-S Spitfire FSM (BAPC.242) [AZ-G]		'42
☐	EE549	Gloster Meteor IV Special		'45
☐	WA984	Gloster Meteor F.8		'51
☐	WB188	Hawker P.1067		'51
☐	WK281	V-S Swift FR.5 [S]		'56
☐	'XF314'	Hawker Hunter F.51 (E-412)		'56
☐	XN299	Westland Whirlwind HAR.7	US	'60
☐	19252	Lockheed T-33A 'T-Bird'	US	'51

Nearby:

Chichester, *3 miles.*

Goodwood House and Circuit, *3 miles.*

Hollycombe House Steam Collection, *16 miles.*

Museum of D-Day Aviation and Shoreham Aerodrome, *20 miles – see page 76.*

City of Portsmouth, *18 miles.*

Swift FR.5 WK281, on loan from the RAF Museum, on display at Tangmere. Ken Ellis

ALSO IN SOUTH EAST ENGLAND

The **MEDWAY AIRCRAFT PRESERVATION SOCIETY** have their workshops at Rochester Airport, Kent. Currently work involves a Spitfire Ia and a Fairchild Argus for the RAF Museum and the restoration of the aerodynamic trials Short Sherpa prototype. The workshop facilities are open to the public on Sundays, Mondays and Wednesdays 9am to 1pm. Airport rules must be observed – the threshold of Runway 34 needs negotiating. SAE to Lewis Deal, 15 Amethyst Avenue, Chatham, Kent, ME5 9TX, 'phone or Fax: 01634 816492.

PETER VALLANCE COLLECTION at Charlwood in Surrey, close to Gatwick Airport, includes two Sea Princes, two Shackletons, a Pembroke C.1, Sea Hawk, Meteor T.7, Canberra PR.7, Gannet

AEW.3 and others. Viewing by prior appointment, contact: Vallance By-Ways, Lowfield Heath Industrial Estate, Westfield Road, Lowfield Heath, Charlwood, Surrey, RH6 0BT. Telephone: 01293 862915.

The **ROBERTSBRIDGE AVIATION SOCIETY** have established their extensive and fascinating collection of airframes and artefacts at the Bush Barn, Robertsbridge, East Sussex. They have also staged an exhibition at Newhaven Fort (see page 77). Airframes held include a Tiger Moth under restoration, the nose sections of a Hunter F.2, Lightning F.3, Sea Vixen FAW.1 and Sukhoi Su-7, plus a wide selection of engines and thousands of artefacts and illustrations. Open by appointment, contact: Philip Baldock, 31 The Rose Walk, Newhaven, East Sussex, BN9 9NJ.

The arrival of Hurricane II 'BN230' at the Hurricane and Spitfire Memorial Building, Manston (see page 73). This painstaking restoration was undertaken by the Medway Aircraft Preservation Society at Rochester. *RAF Manston*

SOUTHERN ENGLAND
Berkshire, Buckinghamshire, Hampshire, Isle of Wight, Oxfordshire

1. Bletchley Park
2. 'Blue Max' Museum of Film Flying
3. Museum of Berkshire Aviation
4. Newbury District Museum
5. Airborne Forces Museum
6. Museum of Army Flying
7. Second World War Aircraft Preservation Society
8. Hall of Aviation Southampton
9. Island Aeroplane Collection

Southern Tourist Board
40 Chamberlayne Road, Eastleigh, Hampshire, SO5 5JH
Tel: 01703 620006 Fax: 01703 620010

AIRBORNE FORCES MUSEUM

Aldershot, Hampshire

Address: Browning Barracks, Aldershot, Hampshire, GU11 2BU.
Telephone: 01252 349619, Fax: 01252 349203.
Where: Signposted off the A325 in Aldershot.
Open: Daily, 10am to 4.30pm. Last admission 3.30pm. Special group visits by prior arrangement.
By bus: Several bus services pass close by.
By rail: Aldershot 1 mile.
Tourist: Aldershot 01252 320968.
Admission: Adult £2.50, OAP/Child £1.
Facilities: Toilets/Parking/Cafe/Shop/Disabled/Kids/All/Changes/Brochure.

With a Douglas Dakota on show outside the museum and substantial elements of two assault gliders from the Second World War, the museum serves to chart the history of Britain's airborne forces and their many campaigns. Large series of displays including post-war campaigns, vehicles, equipment and personalities.

Aircraft exhibits:

☐ KP208	Douglas Dakota IV	US '44
☐ –	Airspeed Horsa II nose	'42
☐ –	GAL Hotspur II nose	'41

Nearby:

Brooklands Museum, *16 miles – see page 71.*
Hollycombe House Steam Collection, *12 miles.*
Mid-Hants Railway, *16 miles.*
Museum of Berkshire Aviation, *16 miles – see page 86.*
REME Museum, Arborfield, *14 miles.*
Second World War Aircraft Preservation Society, *14 miles – see page 88.*
Windsor Castle and Safari Park, *16 miles.*

BLETCHLEY PARK COMMUNICATIONS & ELECTRONICS MUSEUM

Bletchley, Milton Keynes, Bucks

Address: Bletchley Park Trust, The Mansion, Bletchley Park, Bletchley, MK3 6EF.
Telephone: 01908 640404.
  E-mail: tsale@qutaro.demon.co.uk
  Web-site: http://www.cranfield.ac.uk/ccc.uk
Where: Close to Bletchley station, off the B4034.
Open: Every other weekend (eg for 1998, 2nd/3rd May, 16th/17th May etc) 10.30am to 5pm Saturdays and Sundays. Series of special events during the year – SAE for details.
By bus: Bletchley bus station, variety of services, is close by.
By rail: Bletchley station, walking distance.
Tourist: Milton Keynes 01908 232525, Fax: 01908 235050.
Admission: Adult £3.50, Child & OAP £2.
Facilities: Toilets/Parking/All/Changes

Dubbed 'Britain's Best Kept Secret', the mansion and its surroundings are embedded in military history as the home of the 'code breakers' and the computer Colossus. As well as many other exhibits, there is a fascinating Cryptology Museum. The Buckinghamshire Aircraft Recovery Group have established a large collection of aviation memorabilia on display within the historic site, best known for its code-breaking activities during the Second World War. The collection includes uniforms, flying equipment, engines from 'digs' and the nose section of a Jet Provost T.4. A Sea Vixen nose is also stored, it will become an avionics exhibit.

Aircraft exhibits:

☐ XN651	DH Sea Vixen FAW.2 nose	§	'61
☐ XS181	Hunting Jet Provost T.4 nose [F]		'63

'BLUE MAX' MUSEUM OF FILM FLYING

Wycombe Air Park, Buckinghamshire

Address: Wycombe Air Park, Marlow, Bucks, SL7 3DP.

Telephone: 01494 529432 or 01494 449810 or Fax: 01494 461236.

Where: Wycombe Air Park (or Booker), off the B482 south of High Wycombe.

Open: Open Wednesdays and Sundays, March to November, 10am to 5pm.

By bus: Bus service from High Wycombe.

By rail: High Wycombe 3 miles.

Tourist: Marlow* 01628 483597. High Wycombe 01494 421892.

Admission: Adult £2.50, OAP/Child £1.50.

Facilities: Toilets/Parking/Shop/All/Changes.

Run by Bianchi Aviation Film Services (BAFS), specialist film aviation service suppliers for many years, the museum is unique this side of the Atlantic. Aircraft and artefacts from a range of films are on show, including *Those Magnificent Men in Their Flying Machines*, *The Battle of Britain*, *Indiana Jones and the Last Crusade* and *The Blue Max*, from which the museum takes its name. Major changes carried out during the winter of 1994-95 have resulted in a series of set-pieces using 'star' aircraft and placing them in an even more vivid movie setting. Please note that many of the aircraft are airworthy and it may well be that not all of the aircraft in the following list are available at any one time.

Aircraft exhibits:

☐ G-AWXZ	SNCAN SV-4C ✈		Bel '46
☐ G-AZTR	SNCAN SV-4C ✈		Bel '46
☐ G-BAAF	Manning-Flanders MF.1 repro		'12
☐ G-BPVE	Blériot XI repro ✈		Fr '09
☐ 'B2458'	Sopwith Camel repro ✈ (G-BPOB) [R]		'17
☐ 'MS824'	Morane Saulnier 'N' repro ✈ (G-AWBU)		Fr '14
☐ '422/15'	Fokker E.III repro ✈ (G-AVJO)		Gr '15
☐ '626/18'	Travel Air 2000 (N6268)		§'US 25
☐ –	Hulton hang-glider (BAPC.103)		'69
☐ –	Pilatus P.2 fuselage, film mock-up		Sws c50
☐ –	Waxflatter Ornithopter (BAPC.238)		c76

Also:

Wycombe Air Park is a busy light aviation, helicopter and gliding airfield and the tower building offers a good cafe and vantage point to see flying taking place. The aerodrome is also the home of Tiger Fly who undertake pleasure flights from the airfield using a Tiger Moth in Second World War camouflage – prior booking necessary.

Nearby:

Museum of Berkshire Aviation, *14 miles – see page 86.*

Railway Centre, Waddesdon, *18 miles.*

Windsor Castle and Safari Park, *12 miles.*

Supermarine S.6A N248 and the Schneider Trophy on show at the Hall of Aviation, Southampton. Ken Ellis

HALL OF AVIATION
Southampton, Hampshire

Address: Albert Road South, Southampton, SO1 1FR.
Telephone: 0703 635830, Fax: 01703 223383.
Where: Close to Ocean Village and the Itchen Bridge, signed off the A36 in the southern part of the city centre.
Open: Daily Tuesday to Saturday, 10am to 5pm and Sunday 2pm to 5pm. Open Mondays 10am to 5pm during school holidays *only*.
By bus: Several services.
By rail: Southampton Central 1 mile.
Tourist: 01703 221106, Fax: 01703 631437.
Admission: Adult £3, OAP £2, Child £1.50.
Facilities: Toilets/Parking*/Shop/Disabled/All/ Brochure.

The area around Southampton and the Solent is steeped in aviation history and the hall illustrates this heritage vividly, being dominated by the Sandringham flying-boat which stands for the impressive machines that flew from the Solent to all points of the globe from the 1920s to the mid-1950s. Supermarine is synonymous with the area, the prototype Spitfire making its first flight from Southampton Airport in 1936. Airspeed, Avro, Britten Norman, de Havilland, Folland, Saunders-Roe and small concerns like Wight all have local connections and their stories are charted in the many displays.

Aircraft exhibits:

☐ G-ALZE	Britten Norman BN-1F	'51
☐ VH-BRC	Short Sandringham 4	'43
☐ N248	Supermarine S.6A	'29
☐ 'N546'	Wight Quadruplane replica (BAPC.164)	'16
☐ 'C4451'	Avro 504J replica (BAPC.210)	'17
☐ BB807	DH Tiger Moth (G-ADWO)	'35
☐ PK683	V-S Spitfire F.24	'46
☐ TG263	SARO SR.A1 jet flying-boat	'47
☐ WK570	DHC Chipmunk T.10 cockpit	Can '52
☐ WM571	DH Sea Venom FAW.22	'54
☐ WZ753	Slingsby Grasshopper TX.1	'55
☐ XD235	V-S Scimitar F.1	'59
☐ XD596	DH Vampire T.11	§ '54

Short Sandringham 4 VH-BRC dominates the Hall of Aviation. Ken Ellis

☐ XJ476	DH Sea Vixen FAW.1 nose	'57
☐ XK740	Folland Gnat F.1	'56
☐ XL770	SARO Skeeter AOP.12	'60
☐ XN246	Slingsby Cadet TX.3	'62
☐ –	Airwave hang glider (BAPC.215)	c78
☐ –	SUMPAC man-powered aircraft (BAPC.7)	'61

Nearby:
Isle of Wight, *16 miles (ferry)*.
Maritime Museum and the Ocean Village Marina, *walking distance*.
Mid-Hants Railway, *20 miles*.
Museum of Army Flying, *20 miles, see below*.
National Motor Museum, *6 miles*.

MUSEUM OF ARMY FLYING
Middle Wallop Airfield, Hampshire

Address: Middle Wallop, Stockbridge, Hampshire, SO20 8DY.
Telephone: 01980 674421, Fax: 01264 781694.
Where: Middle Wallop Airfield, on the A343 south west of Andover.
Open: 10am to 4.30pm every day.
By bus: Hampshire No 7516 and the Sunday Rider No 9012 stop outside.
By rail: Andover 5 miles.
Tourist: Andover 01264 324320.
Admission: Adult £3.75, OAP £2.75, Child £2.25, Family £10.
Facilities: Toilets/Parking/Cafe/Shop/Disabled/ Kids/All/Changes/Brochure.

Army aviation is the oldest form of military flying in the UK and via its impressive display halls the museum tells the story from man-lifting kites and gas balloons through to the advent of the awesome new attack helicopter shortly to be chosen for today's Army Air Corps. The days of 'eyes for the guns' and the Austers and the 'silent messengers' of the Glider Pilot Regiment are given vivid full-size dioramas. The development of the helicopter is shown from the earliest experiments. The museum car park and the excellent cafe both afford superb views of the fixed wing and helicopter activity on Middle Wallop airfield, the headquarters of the Army Air Corps. A special gallery allows visitors to glimpse into the restoration

workshop. Special exhibitions and events are frequently staged.

Aircraft exhibits:

☐ G-AXKS	Westland-Bell 47G-4A	US '69
☐ 'B-415'	AFEE 10/42 'Rotajeep' repro (BAPC.163)	'42
☐ P-5	Hafner Rotachute AR.III	'42
☐ '5964'	Airco DH.2 repro (BAPC.112)	'16

Below: Airspeed Horsa assault glider in 'just landed' pose at the Museum of Army Flying. Ken Ellis

☐ D7560	Avro 504K	'17
☐ 'F943'	RAF SE.5A scale repro (G-BIHF)	'18
☐ 'N5195'	Sopwith Pup (G-ABOX)	'17
☐ 'KJ351'	Airspeed Horsa II fuselage (BAPC.80)	'42
☐ TJ569	Auster 5 (G-AKOW)	'45
☐ TK777	GAL Hamilcar I fuselage	'44
☐ WG432	DHC Chipmunk T.10 [L]	'51
☐ WJ358	Auster AOP.6 (G-ARYD)	'52
☐ WZ721	Auster AOP.9	'51
☐ WZ772	Slingsby Grasshopper TX.1	'52
☐ XG502	Bristol Sycamore HR.14	'55
☐ XK776	ML Utility Mk 1	'55
☐ XL813	SARO Skeeter AOP.12	'59
☐ 'XM819'	E Percival Prospector	'58
☐ XP821	DHC Beaver AL.1	Can '62
☐ XP822	DHC Beaver AL.1	Can '62
☐ XP847	Westland Scout AH.1	'61
☐ XR232	Sud Alouette AH.2	Fr '60

☐ XT108	Bell Sioux AH.1 (Agusta)	US '66
☐ AE-409	Bell UH-1H Iroquois	US '72
☐ 450/17	Fokker DR.I repro (G-BVGZ)	Gr '17
☐ 111989	Cessna L-19A Bird Dog	US '51
☐ '243809'	WACO CG-4A Hadrian (BAPC.185) [10]	US c44
☐ –	Airspeed Horsa II fuselage	'42
☐ –	Airspeed Horsa II cockpit	'42
☐ –	Hafner R-II (BAPC.10)	Aust '32
☐ –	Westland Scout cabin	c66

Nearby:
Hall of Aviation and city of Southampton,
20 miles, see page 84.
Mid-Hants Railway, 20 miles.
Newbury District Museum, 18 miles – see page 87.
Stonehenge, 18 miles.

MUSEUM OF BERKSHIRE AVIATION

Woodley, Berkshire

Address: Mohawk Way (off Bader Way),
Woodley, near Reading, Berkshire, RG5 4UF.
Telephone: 01189 340712, recorded information
line 01189 9448089.
Where: At Woodley, east of Reading.
Open: Saturdays, Sundays and Bank Holidays
March to October, 10.30am to 5pm. During
May, June and July also open Wednesdays to
Fridays 11.30am to 4pm. October to March
Sundays only 12 noon to 4pm.
By bus: Nos 63/65 come close to the museum.
By rail: Reading 2 miles.
Tourist: 01189 566226, Fax: 01189 566719.
Admission: Adult £2, OAP/Child £1.
Facilities: Toilets/Parking/Cafe/Shop/Disabled/
All/Changes/Brochure.

The former airfield at Woodley, which is close to
the site of the museum, was the home of the hal-
lowed firms of Miles Aircraft and later Handley
Page and the museum serves to highlight the history of the airfield, the aircraft flown and built there
and of the aviation heritage of the county. Access
to the Herald can be achieved most weekends.

Aircraft exhibits:

☐ G-APLK	Miles Student 2	'57
☐ G-APWA	HP Herald 100	'59
☐ TF-SHC	Miles Martinet TT.I wreckage	'43
☐ 6W-SAF	Douglas C-47A Skytrain nose	US '42
☐ 'L6906'	Miles Magister I (BAPC.44)	'39
☐ XG883	Fairey Gannet T.5	'58
☐ XJ389	Fairey Jet Gyrodyne	'47
☐ –	Broburn Wanderlust (BAPC.233)	'46
☐ –	Rogallo-type hang glider	c75

Nearby:
Airborne Forces Museum, 14 miles – see page 82.
'Blue Max' Museum of Film Flying, 14 miles –
see page 83.
Second World War Aircraft Preservation Society,
18 miles – see page 88.
West Berkshire Museum, 20 miles – see page 87.

Glider's eye view of the Second World War Aircraft Preservation Society aircraft park at Lasham. Ken Ellis

SECOND WORLD WAR AIRCRAFT PRESERVATION SOCIETY

Lasham Aerodrome, Hampshire

Address: Bob Coles, 8 Barracane Drive, Crowthorne, Berkshire, RG45 7NU.
Where: Located to the east of the gliding headquarters, on the north side of Lasham aerodrome, near Alton. Access from the A3349 south of Odiham, turn at the 'Golden Pot'.
Open: Open Sundays and Bank Holidays 10am to 6pm (or dusk if first) and other times by arrangement.
By rail: Alton 8 miles.
Tourist: Basingstoke 01256 817618.
Admission: Free, donations welcomed.
Facilities: Parking/Shop/Brochure.

A long-established preservation group with a large aircraft display park including two NATO types, a former Israeli Meteor and the only DHA Drover in the northern hemisphere. Interior displays cover recovered items from Second World War crash sites in the region. As well as the aircraft and artefact collection, the museum offers a commanding view of the intensive gliding activity on the airfield. Trial lessons are available from the Lasham Gliding Society building.

Aircraft exhibits:

☐ 'VH-FDT'	DHA Drover II (G-APXX)	Aus '51
☐ 4X-FNA	Gloster Meteor NF.13	'53
☐ VR192	Percival Prentice 1 (G-APIT)	'48
☐ WF137	Percival Sea Prince C.1	'50
☐ WH291	Gloster Meteor F.8	'51
☐ WV798	Hawker Sea Hawk FGA.6 [026]	'54
☐ XK418	Auster AOP.9	'56
☐ XM833	Westland Wessex HAS.3	US '60
☐ E-423	Hawker Hunter F.51	'56
☐ 22+35	Lockheed F-104G Starfighter	US '61

Nearby:
Airborne Forces Museum, *12 miles, see page 82.*
Hollycombe House Steam Collection, *14 miles.*
Museum of Berkshire Aviation, *20 miles –*
* see page 86.*
City of Winchester, *15 miles.*

WEST BERKSHIRE MUSEUM

Newbury, Berkshire

Address: The Wharf, Newbury, Berks, RG14 5AS.
Telephone: 01635 30511.
E-mail: ktaylor@westberks.gov.uk
Where: The Wharf, Newbury, signed in the centre of the town.
Open: Open April to September Monday to Saturday 10am to 5pm, Sunday and Bank Holidays 1pm to 5pm. OCtober to March Monday to Saturday only 10am to 4pm. Note, closed every Wed – except school holidays.
By bus and rail: Newbury, walking distance.
Tourist: (in museum entrance hall) 01635 30267, Fax: 01635 519562.
Admission: Free.
Facilities: Shop/Disabled*/All/Brochure.
* No access to the Balloon display on first floor.

Using artefacts on loan from the British Balloon Museum and Library plus slides and other material, the museum shows the history of ballooning from 1783 to the present day. Other topics covered by displays in the museum include canals, crafts and industries costume, the civil war etc.

Aircraft exhibits:

☐	G-BBGZ	Cambridge hot air balloon basket	'73
☐	G-BHKR	Colt 14A Cloudhopper hot air balloon	'80
☐	–	Military Gas balloon basket	c41

Nearby:
Didcot Railway Centre, *16 miles.*
Museum of Berkshire Aviation, *20 miles – see page 86.*

Also:
The British Balloon Museum and Library holds an annual 'inflation day' for historic balloons, near Newbury. SAE to: BBML, 3 Chancel Road, Locks Heath, Southampton, SO31 6TF.

ALSO IN SOUTHERN ENGLAND

At **ROYAL NAVAL AIR STATION FLEETLANDS**, near Gosport, Hampshire, is a fine museum tracing the history of the base; included is a Sea Vixen FAW.1 and a Whirlwind HAS.7. Viewing is by prior arrangement only, contact the Curator, RNAY Fleetlands Museum, Gosport, Hampshire, or telephone: 01707 822351, ext 44391.

Note:

The **ISLAND AEROPLANE COMPANY** at Sandown Aerodrome, Isle of Wight, opened its museum to the public during the summer of 1996 with an array of aircraft, mostly flyable. During March 1998,the museum announced it was closing as such and the aircraft were being dispersed as *Aviation Museums of Britain* closed for press. There were hopes to re-open, in another aviation format, during late 1998. (Readers should check with the Sandown Tourist Information Centre – 01983 403886 – for any developments.)

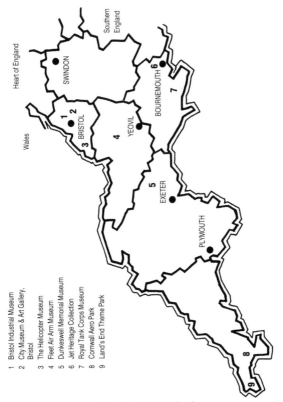

WEST COUNTRY
City of Bristol, Cornwall, Devon, Dorset, Somerset, Wiltshire

Heart of England

Wales

Southern England

SWINDON

BRISTOL

YEOVIL

BOURNEMOUTH

EXETER

PLYMOUTH

1 Bristol Industrial Museum
2 City Museum & Art Gallery, Bristol
3 The Helicopter Museum
4 Fleet Air Arm Museum
5 Dunkeswell Memorial Museum
6 Jet Heritage Collection
7 Royal Tank Corps Museum
8 Cornwall Aero Park
9 Land's End Theme Park

West Country Tourist Board
60 St David's Hill, Exeter, Devon, EX4 4SY
Tel: 01392 76351 Fax: 01392 420891

BRISTOL INDUSTRIAL MUSEUM

Bristol, Gloucestershire

Address: Prince's Wharf, Bristol, BS1 4RN.
Telephone: 0117 9251470, Fax: 0117 9297318.
Where: On Prince's Wharf, south of the A4044 inner ring and well signed from the city centre.
Open: April to October Saturday to Wednesday 10am to 5pm. November to March Saturday and Sunday only, 10am to 5pm
By bus: No 511 passes close. Any others to the city centre, then 10 minutes walk.
By rail: Temple Meads, 10 minutes walk.
Tourist: Bristol 0117 9260767, Fax: 0117 297703.
Admission: Adult £1.05, Cons 50p, Children free.
Facilities: Toilets/Parking/Shop/Disabled/All/ Brochure.

As well as the Sycamore helicopter, there is a fabulous array of Bristol aero engines on show – many having been restored by the Rolls-Royce Heritage Trust, Bristol Branch – see page 99. Also here is a 'walk-through' engineering mock-up of Concorde. Within the museum are displays on the local docks and an excellent road transport section. Located on the 'Floating harbour' element of the River Avon, the museum offers superb views of the river and the buildings around.

Aircraft exhibit:

☐ XL829	Bristol Sycamore HR.14	'57
☐ –	BAC/SNIAS Concorde fuselage	'70

Nearby:

Avon Valley Railway, *5 miles.*
City of Bath, *12 miles.*
SS *Great Britain* and Maritime Heritage Centre, *10 minutes walk down the quayside.*
The Helicopter Museum, *20 miles – see page 94.*
City Museum and Art Gallery, *1 mile – see opposite.*

CITY MUSEUM AND ART GALLERY

Bristol, Gloucestershire

Address: Queen's Road, Clifton, Bristol, BS8 1RL.
Telephone: 0117 9223571, Fax: 0117 9222047. Web-site: http://www.bristol-city.gov.uk
Where: On the A4018 to the west of the city centre, near the University.
Open: Every day including Sundays, 10am to 5pm.
By bus: Many bus routes possible.
By rail: Temple Meads, short walk.
Tourist: Bristol 0117 9260767, Fax: 0117 297703.
Admission: Adult £2.10, Cons £1.05, Child free.
Facilities: Toilets/Parking/Cafe/Shop/Disabled/ All/Changes/Brochure.

Suspended within the foyer of this delightful building is a Bristol Boxkite replica and there are other aviation artefacts on show, detailing aviation in Bristol. Worldwide collections representing the arts, human history and the natural sciences.

Aircraft exhibit:

☐ –	Bristol Boxkite replica (BAPC.40)	'10

Nearby:

Avon Valley Railway, *5 miles.*
City of Bath, *12 miles.*
Bristol Industrial Museum, *1 mile – see opposite.*
SS *Great Britain* and Maritime Heritage Centre, *10 minutes walk down the quayside.*
The Helicopter Museum, *20 miles – see page 94.*

Also:

For both **Bristol** locations, **Bristol Balloons** offer pleasure flights, subject to weather throughout the year. Contact: Parklands Road, Bristol, BS3 2JW, or telephone: 0117 9637858.

CORNWALL AERO PARK AND FLAMBARDS THEME PARK
Helston, Cornwall

Address: Clodgey Lane, Helston, Cornwall, TR13 0GA.
Telephone: 01326 564093, Fax: 01326 573344.
Where: Signed off the A3083 south of Helston, alongside RNAS Culdrose.
Open: Every day Easter to end of October 10am to 5pm. Last admission 3.30pm.
By bus: Western National stops within the museum.
By rail: Redruth 12 miles.
Tourist: On site* 01326 565431. Falmouth 01326 312300, Fax: 01326 313457.
Admission: Adult £6.95, Child £6.25, Seniors (over 55) £4.50.
Facilities: Toilets/Parking/Cafe/Shop/Disabled/ Kids/All/ Changes/Brochure.

The aeronautical collection is part of a larger attraction, the Flambards Village Theme Park. Views of the flying underway at the Royal Naval Air Station Culdrose are easily achieved from the museum. The site park includes a wide range of entertainment and rides plus an Edwardian theme village.

Aircraft exhibits:

☐ G-BDDX	Whittaker Excalibur homebuild		'76
☐ WF122	Percival Sea Prince T.1 [575-CU]		
☐ WG511	Avro Shackleton T.4 nose		'52
☐ 'WG754'	Westland Dragonfly HR.5 (WG725) [912-CU]		US '52
☐ WK122	EE Canberra TT.18 [22]		'54
☐ XA870	Westland Whirlwind HAS.1	§ US '54
☐ XD332	V-S Scimitar F.1 [194-C]		'60
☐ XE368	Hawker Sea Hawk FGA.6 [200-J]		'55
☐ XG831	Fairey Gannet ECM.6 [396]		'56
☐ XN647	DH Sea Vixen FAW.2 [707-VL]		'61
☐ XP350	Westland Whirlwind HAR.10		US '62
☐ XS887	Westland Wessex HAS.1 [403-Fl]	US '66
☐ XT427	Westland Wasp HAS.1 [606]		'65

Nearby:
Falmouth, *10 miles.*
Hayle Towans Railway, *10 miles.*
Lappa Valley Railway, *20 miles.*
Land's End Theme Park, *18 miles – see page 98.*

DUNKESWELL MEMORIAL MUSEUM
Dunkeswell Aerodrome, Devon

Address: Dunkeswell Memorial Museum, Dunkeswell Aerodrome, Honiton, Devon, EX14 0RA.
Telephone: 01404 841843.
Where: At Dunkeswell Aerodrome, north of Honiton. Signposted.
Open: Tuesday to Sunday 10am to 6.30pm, other times by prior appointment.
Tourist: Honiton 01404 43716.
Admission: Adult £1.00, child 50p.
Facilities: Toilets/Parking/Cafe*.

Opened up to the public duringf 1997, having been formally brought into being in August 1995. It is dedicated to the history of the airfield and its resident units, the Consolidated PB4Y-1 equipped FAW-7 of the US Navy. The centre of the museum is a collection of local artefacts, amassed since the early 1980s by the founders, David Sharland, Darren Lillywhite and Rupert Fairclough.

Aircraft exhibits:

☐ XE982	DH Vampire T.11	'55
☐ –	Fairey Gannet cockpit section.	c53

Nearby:
Exeter and Exeter Airport, 15 miles.
Grand Western Canal, 8 miles.

FLEET AIR ARM MUSEUM

Yeovilton Airfield, Somerset

Address: RNAS Yeovilton, Ilchester, Somerset, BA22 8HT.

Telephone: 01935 840565, Fax: 01935 840181

Where: Well signed off the A303 west of Wincanton.

Open: Every day (other than Xmas) April to October 10am to 5.30pm (last 'flights' to 'Carrier' 4pm and November to February 10am to 4.30pm (last 'flights' to 'Carrier' 3pm).

By bus: Regular services into Ilchester, 2 miles.

By rail: Yeovil 6 miles.

Tourist: Podimore* 01935 841302. Yeovil 01935 71279, Fax: 01935 34065.

Admission: Adult £6.80, child £4.50, seniors £5.80, family ticket £18.00.

Facilities: Toilets/Parking/Cafe/Shop/Disabled/ Kids/All/Changes/Brochure.

Dominating this large and vibrant museum is the incredible 'Carrier' exhibition in which visitors are 'flown' inside a Wessex helicopter onto the flight deck of an aircraft carrier after which they can roam the aircraft exhibits on the flight deck and go for a 'guided' tour of the 'island' – ending up at the bridge and 'FlyCo's' station. Complete with mannequin guide and soundtrack and special effects. As if this were not enough four galleries take the visitor through the entire history of naval aviation from the mud-splattered First World War section, to the bamboo of the Korean war exhibit, to the 'ski-jump' reconstruction in the vertical take-off section. Then there is the British Concorde prototype and the development aircraft that helped it on its way and these will centre in a new exhibition entitled 'Milestones of Flight'. A restoration and storage centre – allowing the public a view – is also planned. A special gallery in the museum affords excellent views of the activity on the busy naval air station.

Aircraft exhibits:

☐	'G-ABUL'	DH Tiger Moth (XL717)	'40
☐	G-BSST	BAC/SNIAS Concorde 002	UK/Fr '69
☐	8359	Short 184 fuselage	'15
☐	'B6401'	Sopwith Camel repro (G-AWYY)	'17
☐	L2301	Supermarine Walrus I	'39
☐	L2940	Blackburn Skua I wreck	'39
☐	N1854	Fairey Fulmar II	'39
☐	'N2078'	Sopwith Baby floatplane replica	'15
☐	'N4389'	Fairey Albacore I (N4172) [4M]	'40
☐	'N5492'	Sopwith Triplane repro (BAPC.111)	'17
☐	'N6452'	Sopwith Pup repro (G-BIAU)	'17
☐	'P4139'	Fairey Swordfish II (HS618)	'43
☐	'S1287'	Fairey Flycatcher repro	c25
☐	AL246	Grumman Martlet I	US '40
☐	DP872	Fairey Barracuda II fuselage	'41
☐	EX976	NA Harvard IIA	US '41
☐	KD431	Vought Corsair IV [E2-M]	US '44
☐	KE209	Grumman Hellcat II	US '44
☐	LZ551/G	DH Sea Vampire I	'45
☐	SX137	V-S Seafire F.17	'45
☐	VH127	Fairey Firefly TT.4	'47
☐	VR137	Westland Wyvern TF.1	'47
☐	WA473	V-S Attacker F.1 [102-J]	'51
☐	WG774	BAC 221 ogival wing research aircraft	'52
☐	WJ231*	Hawker Sea Fury FB.11 [115-O]	'50
☐	WN493	Westland Dragonfly HR.5	US '53
☐	WT121	Douglas Skyraider AEW.1	§ US '51
☐	WV856	Hawker Sea Hawk FGA.6	'54
☐	WW138	DH Sea Venom FAW.22 [227-Z]	'55
☐	XA127	DH Sea Vampire T.22 nose	'54
☐	XB446	Grumman Avenger ECM.6B	US '45
☐	XD317	V-S Scimitar F.1 [112]	'59
☐	XG900	Short SC.1	'57
☐	XJ314	Rolls-Royce Thrust Measuring Rig ('Flying Bedstead')	'53
☐	XK488	Blackburn Buccaneer S.1	'58
☐	XL503	Fairey Gannet AEW.3 [070-E]	'60
☐	XL580*	Hawker Hunter T.8M [723]	'58
☐	XN957	Blackburn Buccaneer S.1 [630-LM]	'63
☐	XP841	HP.115 delta research aircraft	'61
☐	XP980	Hawker P.1127	'63
☐	XS508	Westland Wessex HU.5	US '64

Above: 'MiG-15' amid the Korean war exhibit. Ken Ellis   Below: **Inside the control room on board 'Carrier'.** FAAM

☐	XS527	Westland Wasp HAS.1	'63
☐	XS590	DH Sea Vixen FAW.2 [131-E]	'66
☐	XT482	Westland Wessex HU.5 [ZM]	US '66
☐	XT596	McDD Phantom FG.1	US '66
☐	XT769	Westland Wessex HU.5 [823-CU]	US '66
☐	XV333	HS Buccaneer S.2B [234-H]	'66
☐	WX890	Westland Gazelle HT.2	Fr '74
☐	AE-422	Bell UH-1H Iroquois	US '74
☐	'D.5397'	Albatros D.Va repro (G-BFXL)	Gr '17
☐	'102 /17'	Fokker Dr I scale repro (BAPC.88)	Gr '17

☐	15-1585	Yokosuka MXY-7 Ohka 11	
		suicide weapon (BAPC.58)	Ja '45
☐	01420	MiG MiG-15bis / Lim-2 (G-BMZF)	Ru c55
☐	159233	HS AV-8A Harrier [33-CG]	'74
☐	–	Fairey IIIF fuselage frame	'27
☐	–	Short S.27 repro (BAPC.149)	§ '10

Nearby:

East Somerset Railway, *12 miles*.
Haynes Motor Museum, *2 miles*.

THE HELICOPTER MUSEUM
Weston-super-Mare, Avon

Address: Weston Airport, Locking Moor Road,
Weston-super-Mare, Avon, BS22 8PP.
Telephone: 01934 635227, Fax: 01934 822400.
E-mail: hellicopte@aol.com
Web-site: http://www.dialspace.dial.pipex.com/
town/terrace/aaa76
Where: On the A371 east of Weston and well
signposted.
Open: April to October, daily 10am to 6pm.
November to March, Wed to Sun 10am to 4pm.
By bus: Helibus 120, 121 and 126 from Weston
sea front.
By rail: Milton Halt, 1 mile.
Tourist: Weston-super-Mare 01934 626838,
Fax: 01934 612006.
Admission: Adult £3.00, OAP £2.50, Child £2.00,
Family ticket £8.00.
Facilities: Toilets/Parking/Cafe/Shop/Disabled/
All/Changes/Brochure.

The truly international flavour continues with the
acquisition of further examples of rotorcraft from
around the world, with still more 'in the pipeline'.
The Helicopter Museum holds the world's largest
rotary wing collection. A new display gallery has
been opened. There is an extensive workshop with
several helicopters always receiving attention – the
public can watch progress. Some of the airframes,
including the recently-arrived WG.30s are 'stock'

for trades and exchanges and may not stay long
with the collection. Inside displays include the history of helicopters, the story of Westland Helicopters, drone helicopters and two man-powered
helicopter exhibits. 'Open Cockpit' days are held
every second Sunday in the month, March to October and the annual 'HeliDays' fly-in is held on the
Weston Sea Front each July. The museum also
stages occasional 'Engineering Days' offering
conducted tours of the workshop. For those so
equipped, the museum has its own one acre heli-
port for flying visitors.

Aircraft exhibits:

☐	D-HMQV	Bölkow Bö 102 Helitrainer	Gr '60
☐	D-HOAY	Kamov Ka-26	Ru c65
☑	F-OCMF	Sud Super Frelon	Fr '67
☐	G-ACWM	Cierva C.30A (Avro)	Sp '35
☐	G-ANFH	Westland Whirlwind Srs 1	§ US '54
☐	G-ANJV	Westland Whirlwind Srs 3	§ US '54
☐	G-AODA	Westland Whirlwind Srs 3	§ US '55
☐	G-AOUJ	Fairey Ultra Light Helicopter	§ '56
☐	G-ARVN	Servotec Grasshopper II	§ '62
☐	G-ASCT	Bensen B.8M gyrocopter	§ US '62
☐	G-ASHD	Brantly B.2A	§ US '63
☐	G-ASOL	Bell 47D-1	§ US '62
☐	G-ASTP	Hiller UH-12C	US '61
☐	G-ATBZ	Westland Wessex 60 Srs 1	§ US '66
☐	G-AVKE	Thruxton Gadfly HDW-1	§ '67
☐	G-AVNE	Westland Wessex 60 Srs 1	US '67
☐	G-AWRP	Cierva Rotorcraft Grasshopper III	§ '69
☐	G-AXFM	Cierva Rotorcraft Grasshopper III rig	§ '70

THE HELICOPTER MUSEUM

Weston-super-Mare, Avon

Address: Weston Airport, Locking Moor Road,
Weston-super-Mare, Avon, BS22 8PP.

Telephone: 01934 635227, Fax: 01934 822400.
E-mail: hellicopte@aol.com
Web-site: http://www.dialspace.dial.pipex.com/
town/terrace/aaa76

Where: On the A371 east of Weston and well
signposted.

Open: April to October, daily 10am to 6pm.
November to March, Wed to Sun 10am to 4pm.

By bus: Helibus 120, 121 and 126 from Weston
sea front.

By rail: Milton Halt, 1 mile.

Tourist: Weston-super-Mare 01934 626838,
Fax: 01934 612006.

Admission: Adult £3.00, OAP £2.50, Child £2.00,
Family ticket £8.00.

Facilities: Toilets/Parking/Cafe/Shop/Disabled/
All/Changes/Brochure.

The truly international flavour continues with the
acquisition of further examples of rotorcraft from
around the world, with still more 'in the pipeline'.
The Helicopter Museum holds the world's largest
rotary wing collection. A new display gallery has
been opened. There is an extensive workshop with
several helicopters always receiving attention – the
public can watch progress. Some of the airframes,
including the recently-arrived WG.30s are 'stock'
for trades and exchanges and may not stay long
with the collection. Inside displays include the history of helicopters, the story of Westland Helicopters, drone helicopters and two man-powered
helicopter exhibits. 'Open Cockpit' days are held
every second Sunday in the month, March to October and the annual 'HeliDays' fly-in is held on the
Weston Sea Front each July. The museum also
stages occasional 'Engineering Days' offering
conducted tours of the workshop. For those so
equipped, the museum has its own one acre heli-
port for flying visitors.

Aircraft exhibits:

☐ D-HMQV	Bölkow Bö 102 Helitrainer	Gr '60
☐ D-HOAY	Kamov Ka-26	Ru c65
☐ F-OCMF	Sud Super Frelon	Fr '67
☐ G-ACWM	Cierva C.30A (Avro)	Sp '35
☐ G-ANFH	Westland Whirlwind Srs 1	§ US '54
☐ G-ANJV	Westland Whirlwind Srs 3	§ US '54
☐ G-AODA	Westland Whirlwind Srs 3	§ US '55
☐ G-AOUJ	Fairey Ultra Light Helicopter	§ '56
☐ G-ARVN	Servotec Grasshopper II	§ '62
☐ G-ASCT	Bensen B.8M gyrocopter	§ US '62
☐ G-ASHD	Brantly B.2A	§ US '63
☐ G-ASOL	Bell 47D-1	§ US '62
☐ G-ASTP	Hiller UH-12C	US '61
☐ G-ATBZ	Westland Wessex 60 Srs 1	§ US '66
☐ G-AVKE	Thruxton Gadfly HDW-1	§ '67
☐ G-AVNE	Westland Wessex 60 Srs 1	US '67
☐ G-AWRP	Cierva Rotorcraft Grasshopper III	§ '69
☐ G-AXFM	Cierva Rotorcraft Grasshopper III rig	§ '70
☐ G-AZAU	Cierva Rotorcraft Grasshopper III rig	§ c71
☐ G-AZBY	Westland Wessex 60 Srs 1	§ US '71
☐ G-AZYB	Bell 47H-1	§ US '56
☐ G-BAPS	Campbell Cougar	§ '73
☐ G-BGHF	Westland WG.30-100	'79
☐ G-HAUL	Westland WG.30-TT300	'86

**Visitors to the The Helicopter Museum can take a peak
into the workshops.** Ken Ellis

Above: **'Star'** among many fascinating exhibits is the world record breaking Lynx 800 G-LYNX. Westland Helicopters

Below: **Jet Heritage** is a working collection with most of the aircraft in airworthy condition. Meteor TT.20 WM167 is a frequent attender at airshows. Jet Heritage.

JET HERITAGE COLLECTION
Bournemouth Airport, Dorset

Address: JHL, Hangar 600, Bournemouth International Airport, Christchurch, Dorset, BH23 7DQ.

Telephone: 01202 581676.

Where: Bournemouth Airport, Hurn. Signposted off the A348 and A338.

Open: April to September 9am to 5pm, October to March 10am to 4pm.

By bus: Details from TIC.

By rail: Bournemouth, 3 miles.

Tourist: Bournemouth 01202 451700, Fax: 01202451743.

Admission: Adult £4.50, OAPs £3.00, child £2.00, family £10.00.

Facilities: Toilets/Parking/Changes/Brochure.

Opened to the public for the first time from Easter 1998, Jet Heritage (JHL) is a working collection of former military jet aircraft, spanning the first and second generations of British jets. Visitors can watch ambitious restoration projects underway.

A series of special events are planned and JHL aircraft can also regularly bee seen at airshows across Europe.

Aircraft exhibits:

☐ G-AGSH	DH Dragon Rapide 6 ✈		'45
☐ G-HVIP	Hawker Hunter T.68 (J-4208) ✈		'56
☐ WM167	Gloster Meteor TT.20 (G-LOSM) ✈		'52
☐ XE677	Hunter Hunter F.4 (G-HHUN) ✈		'55
☐ XF114	V-S Swift F.7 (G-SWIF)		'57
☐ XG160	Hawker Hunter F.6A (G-BWAF) ✈	§	'56
☐ XH328	DH Vampire T.11		'55
☐ XK527	HS Buccaneer S.2B nose		'60
☐ XL600	Hawker Hunter T.7 (G-VETA) ✈		'58
☐ XP627	Hunting Jet Provost T.4 (G-RAFI) [27]		'62
☐ XR537	Folland Gnat T.1 (G-NATY)		'63
☐ XW291	BAC Jet Provost T.5 (G-BWOF) ✈		'69
☐ '215'	DH Vampire T.55 (G-HELV) ✈		'56
☐ ET-273	Hawker Hunter T.7 'gate guardian'		'58
☐ J-4083	Hawker Hunter F.58 (G-EGHH) ✈		'59
☐ J-4104	Hawker Hunter F.58 (G-PSST) ✈		'56

Nearby:
National Motor Museum, Beaulieu, *20 miles*.
The Tank Museum, *20 miles – see page 98*.

LAND'S END THEME PARK
Land's End, Cornwall

Address: Land's End, Sennen, TR19 7AA.

Telephone: 01736 81220, Fax: 01736 871812, information hot-line 01736 871220, Web-site: http://www.landsend-landmark.co.uk

Where: Land's End, on the A30 west of Penzance. Well signed.

Open: Daily (except Xmas) 9am to 6pm.

By bus: From Penzance, 8 miles.

By rail: Penzance, 8 miles.

Tourist: Penzance 01736 62207, Fax: 01736 63600.

Admission: Individual prices for each attraction.

Facilities: Toilets/Parking/Cafe/Shop/Disabled/Kids/All/Changes/Brochure.

With much to appeal to kids of all ages, this legendary site offers a wide array of attractions. From an aeronautical point of view, 1998 sees a new movie presentation on air-sea rescue shot along Cornwall's coastline. Suspended at a dramatic angle within the complex is an MBB 105 in the colours of the Cornwall Air Ambulance, who operate the real thing from nearby St Mawgan.

Aircraft exhibit:

☐ 'G-CDBS'	MBB Bö 105D (G-BCXO)		Gr '75

Nearby:
Beam engine and tin mine, Pendeen, *6 miles*.
Cornwall Aero Park, *18 miles – see page 91*.
Penzance, *10 miles*.

THE TANK MUSEUM
Bovington, Dorset

Address: Bovington, Dorset, BH20 6JG.
Telephone: 01929 405096 or 09129 463953 (recorded message), Fax: 01929 405360.
Where: Signposted from the A352 north of Wool.
Open: Open daily (with some exceptions) 10am to 5pm.
By bus: Local services stop nearby.
By rail: Wool 2 miles.
Tourist: Wareham 01929 552740.
Admission: Adult £6.00, OAP £5.00, child £4.00, family ticket £15.00.
Facilities: Toilets/Parking/Cafe/Shop/Disabled/ Kids/All/Changes.

Over 200 armoured fighting vehicles of many nationalities are on display, plus a huge amount of supporting material. The Hamilcar transport glider section will be used as a centre-piece with a Tetrarch air portable tank. A Skeeter helicopter 'hovers' above the tracked exhibits. There are special events staged throughout the year.

Aircraft exhibits:

☐ TK718	GAL Hamilcar I fuselage	'45
☐ XM564	SARO Skeeter AOP.12	'60

Nearby:
City of Bournemouth, *16 miles.*
Dorchester, *10 miles.*
Jet Heritage Collection, *20 miles – see page 97.*

ALSO
IN THE WEST COUNTRY

ROLLS-ROYCE HERITAGE TRUST, Bristol Branch have established an astounding collection of aero engines, centred on a former test shell building within the Rolls-Royce plant at Filton, Bristol, Avon. Also held is the cockpit of Beagle 206-1 G-ATDD and Aermacchi MB.339AA 0767. Visits are by prior permission only, and well worth it. Contact: Peter Pavey, AITD (GP2/1), Rolls-Royce plc, PO Box 3, Filton, Bristol BS12 7QE.

The **SCIENCE MUSEUM Air Transport Collection and Storage Facility** is at Wroughton airfield, near Swindon, Wiltshire. Housed here is a large collection of airliners of all sizes, plus other items such as agricultural machinery, cars and lorries. Sadly, the number of opportunities for the public to inspect this fine collection are small. Contact 01793 814466.

The **SEA VIXEN SOCIETY** keep DH Sea Vixen FAW.2 XJ580 on public view on the B3059 Somerford Road, at the entrance to the Somerford Road Retail Park, near MFI in Christchurch, Dorset.

YORKSHIRE

East Yorkshire, North Yorkshire, South Yorkshire, West Yorkshire

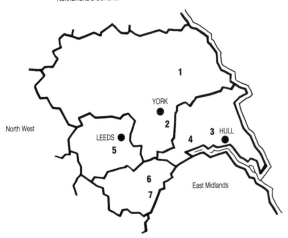

Northumbria & Cumbria

North West

East Midlands

YORK

LEEDS

HULL

1 Eden Camp
2 Yorkshire Air Museum
3 Museum of Army Transport
4 Real Aeroplane Museum
5 Skopos Motor Museum
6 Doncaster Museum
7 South Yorkshire Aircraft Museum

Yorkshire Tourist Board
312 Tadcaster Road, York, YO2 2HF
Tel: 01904 707961   Fax: 01904 701414

DONCASTER MUSEUM AND ART GALLERY
Doncaster, South Yorkshire

Address: Chequer Road, Doncaster, DN1 2AE.
Telephone: 01302 734293, Fax: 01302 735409.
Where: Close to the town centre, well signed.
Open: Open Monday to Saturday 10am to 5pm and Sunday 2pm to 5pm.
By Bus: Bust station, or Waterdale.
By Rail: Doncaster, walking distance.
Tourist: Doncaster, 01302 734309.
Admission: Free.
Facilities: Toilets/Parking/Shop/Disabled/All/ Changes/Brochure.

Atop the main staircase 'flies' a Mignet HM.14 'Flying Flea' that has been built up around surviving parts of an example that was built by a local company and flown from Doncaster Airport 1936-37. The original survived until 1970 when it was gutted in a fire at RAF Finningley. The new airframe, using much of the original, including the Scott 'Flying Squirrel' engine was made at RAF Oakington.

Aircraft exhibit:

☐ 'G-AEKR' HM.14 'Flea' (BAPC.121)   § Fr 36

Nearby
City of Sheffield, 15 miles.
Skopos Motor Museum, 20 miles – see page 102.
South Yorkshire Aircraft Museum, 12 miles – see page 103.

Flying Flea 'G-AEKR' now 'flies' within Doncaster Museum and Art Gallery. Ken Ellis

EDEN CAMP MODERN HISTORY THEME MUSEUM
Old Malton, North Yorkshire

Address: Malton, North Yorkshire, YO17 0SD.
Telephone: 01653 697777, Fax: 01653 698243.
  E-mail: admin@edencamp.co.uk
  Web-site: http://www.edencamp.co.uk
Where: On the A64 York to Scarborough road, north of Malton, near the junction with the A169. Signposted.
Open: Daily 10am to 5pm from February 14 to December 23, last admission 4pm. January to February weekdays only.
By bus: Local services, enquire via local TIC.
By rail: Malton, 1 mile.
Tourist: Malton 01653 600048.
Admission: Adult £3, OAP/child £2.
Facilities: Toilets/Parking/Cafe/Shop/Disabled/ Kids/All/ Changes/Brochure.

Once a prisoner of war camp, now an award-winning museum and theme park. The museum uses extensive and detailed dioramas to tell the story of the Second World War with heavy emphasis on the 'home front'. There is a choice of 'Mess' to eat in, a cinema, even a period war news reading room. Three replica aircraft are displayed and there is a growing collection of operational military vehicles including a T-34 tank and an M16 half-track.

Aircraft exhibits:

☐	'P2793'	Hawker Hurricane repro (BAPC.236) [SD-M]	§ '40
☐	'AA908'	V-S Spitfire repro (BAPC.230) [UM-W]	'41
☐	–	Fieseler Fi 103 (V-1) flying-bomb repro	Gr '45

Nearby:
National Railway Museum, 17 miles.
North Yorkshire Moors Railway, 16 miles.
Yorkshire Air Museum, 17 miles – see page 104.

MUSEUM OF ARMY TRANSPORT

Beverley, East Yorkshire

Address: Flemingate, Beverley, East Yorkshire, HU17 0NG.

Telephone: 01482 860445 Fax: 01482 872767.

Where: In Flemingate, Beverley, well signed within the town, close to the Minster.

Open: 10am to 5pm every day, closed Xmas.

By bus: Regular services from Hull to Beverley.

By rail: Beverley Minister, walking distance.

Tourist: Beverley 01482 867430 or 01482 883898, Fax: 01482 883913.

Admission: Adult £4.00, OAP £2.50, child £2.00, family ticket £10.00.

Facilities: Toilets/Parking/Cafe/Shop/Disabled/ Kids/All/Changes/Brochure.

Drive into the capacious car park of the museum and one item dominates the external displays at Flemingate – the only surviving Blackburn Beverley transport. This huge airlifter is not only an exhibit but serves as an exhibition hall! Within are displays on aerial despatch and on the huge task of moving the aircraft on to site and its restoration. The museum changed hands in 1997 and plans are afoot for its continued development. Within the extensive museum building can be found many of the museum's 200 plus vehicles, including military locomotives, many of which are set in full-scale dioramas. There is also an extensive aircraft model collection set in its own 'house'.

Aircraft exhibit:

☐ XB259   Blackburn Beverley C.1   '55

Nearby:

Beverley Minster and town, *walking distance.*

Humber Bridge and Viewing Area, *9 miles.*

City of Kingston upon Hull, *8 miles.*

Real Aeroplane Museum, *20 miles –*
see page 102.

The Beverley (below) dominates the exterior of the Museum of Army Transport and also serves as an exhibition hall (above)! Both Ken Ellis

REAL AEROPLANE MUSEUM
Breighton Aerodrome, East Yorkshire

Address: Breighton Aerodrome, near Selby,
YO8 7DH.
Telephone: 01757 289065.
Where: In between Bubwith and Breighton, east
of Selby.
Open: 10.30am to 4pm, Sat and Sun. Other times
by prior arrangement.
By rail: Goole, 8 miles.
Tourist: Selby 01757 703263.
Admission: TBA.
Facilities: Toilets/Parking/Cafe.

Located on a portion of a former Bomber Com-
mand airfield, Breighton is a thriving aerodrome
with an active light aircraft population. Visitors can
have a grandstand view of flying activity during their
stay. This is very much a formative museum with a
display building planned. At present, tours of the
hangars and workshops are undertaken and views
of the aircraft held in store for future display can be
occasionally gleaned. The aircraft listed are those
of Tony Smith and friends plus the light aircraft collection of Nigel Ponsford – other aircraft are based.

Aircraft exhibits:

☐ G-AEVS	Aeronca 100 ✈	US '37
☐ G-AOBG	Somers-Kendal SK.1	§ '55
☐ G-AXEI	Ward Gnome	'67
☐ G-BUTX	Bücker (CASA) I-133 Jungmeister	§ Gr c52
☐ G-BWUE	Hispano HA-1112-M1L Buchon	Sp c52
☐ G-TAFF	Bücker (CASA) I-131 Jungmann	Gr c48
☐ 'BE417'	Hawker Hurricane XII ✈ (G-HURR)	[AL-X] '42
☐ PL965	V-S Spitfire PR.XI ✈ (G-MKXI)	'44
☐ XK819	Slingsby Grasshopper TX.1	§ '55
☐ 100502	Focke-Achgelis Fa 330A-1	§ Gr c44

Nearby:
City of Beverley, *20 miles.*
City of York and National Railway Museum,
15 miles.
Museum of Army Transport, *20 miles –*
see page 101.
Yorkshire Air Museum, *12 miles – see page 104.*

SKOPOS MOTOR MUSEUM
Batley, West Yorkshire

Address: Alexander Mills, Alexander Road,
Batley, WF17 6JA.
Telephone: 01924 444423.
Where: Signed within the town.
Open: Open daily 10am to 5pm.
By bus: Refer to TIC.
By rail: Batley, close by.
Tourist: Hartshead Moor, 01274 869167
Admission: TBA.
Facilities: Toilets/Parking/Shop.

The museum previously displayed the Bristol M.1C
Monoplane now at the Shuttleworth Collection. In
late 1997, it took on a new aircraft exhibit, a Luton
Minor single-seat parasol homebuild. An extensive
selection of motor cars are on view.

Aircraft exhibit:

☐ G-AMAW	Luton LA-4 Minor	'50

Nearby:
Doncaster Museum, *20 miles – see page 100.*
Bradford, Halifax, Huddersfield, Leeds and
Huddersfield all close by.

SOUTH YORKSHIRE AVIATION MUSEUM

Firbeck, South Yorkshire

Address: Ian Kingsnorth, South Yorkshire Aviation Society, 21 Broom Grove, Rotherham, South Yorkshire, S60 2TE.

Telephone: 01709 372821.

Where: At Home Farm, off the A364 Maltby to East Retford road, north of Firbeck village.

Open: Open every Sunday and Bank Holidays 10am to 5pm. Other times by arrangement.

By rail: Worksop 6 miles.

Tourist: Worksop 01909 501148, Fax: 01909 501611.

Admission: Free, donations welcomed.

Facilities: Toilets/Parking/Cafe*/Shop/Disabled/All/Changes/Brochure/X.

A lovely setting for a pleasing museum, once the site of the officers' mess of RAF Firbeck. As well as a wide variety of airframes on display in the aircraft park, there is an extensive aero engine collection, ranging from a Liberty of 1918 to the Pegasus that lifts and powers the Harrier. Also a large radio and radar equipment display, uniforms and flying clothing and a wide array of items from aviation archaeology 'digs' in the region.

Aircraft exhibits:

☐ G-ALYB	Auster 5	§	'44
☐ G-APMY	Piper Apache 160	US	'58

☐ G-AVAA	Cessna F.150G	US	'66
☐ TJ707	Auster AOP.6 fuselage		'45
☐ WA662	Gloster Meteor T.7		'50
☐ WB733	DHC Chipmunk T.10	Can	'50
☐ WJ903	Vickers Varsity T.1 nose		'53
☐ WL131	Gloster Meteor F.8 nose		'52
☐ WM367	Gloster Meteor NF.13 nose		'52
☐ WT684	Hawker Hunter F.1		'54
☐ WZ822	Slingsby Grasshopper TX.1		'55
☐ XE317	Bristol Sycamore HR.14		'56
☐ XE935	DH Vampire T.11 [30]		'55
☐ XG297	Hawker Hunter FGA.9 nose	§	'56
☐ XH584	EE Canberra T.4 nose		'55
☐ XL609	Hawker Hunter T.7 nose		'58
☐ XM350	Hunting Jet Provost T.3A [89]		'58
☐ XM561	SARO Skeeter AOP.12		'59
☐ XN238	Slingsby Cadet TX.3		'59
☐ XN511	Hunting Jet Provost T.3 nose		'60
☐ XN597	Hunting Jet Provost T.3 nose		'61
☐ XP190	Westland Scout AH.1		'62
☐ XR754	EE Lightning F.6 nose		'65
☐ XS897	EE Lightning F.6		'66
☐ XT242	Bell Sioux AH.1 (Westland) [12]		'66
☐ E-424	Hawker Hunter F.51		'56
☐ –	DH Vampire FB.5 nose		c50

Nearby:

Doncaster Museum, *12 miles – see page 100*.
National Mining Museum, Bevercotes, *12 miles*.
Cities of Rotherham (16 miles) and Sheffield (20 miles).

A view of the aircraft park at Firbeck, Vampire T.11 and Jet Provost T.4. Ken Ellis

From any angle, *Friday the 13th*, Yorkshire Air Museum's Halifax reconstruction, is impressive. Ken Ellis

YORKSHIRE AIR MUSEUM

Elvington. North Yorkshire

Address: Elvington, York, YO4 5AT.
Telephone: 01904 608595, Fax: 01904 608246.
Where: Signed from the A64 southern York ring road, at the A64/A166/A1079 junction.
Open: Weekdays 10.30am to 4pm, weekends and Bank Holidays 10.30am to 5pm. Other times by arrangement.
By rail: York 5 miles.
Tourist: York 01904 620557, Fax: 01904 620576.
Admission: Adult £4.00, OAP/child £3.00.
Facilities: Toilets/Parking/Cafe/Shop/Disabled/ All/Changes/Brochure.

Set around the former watch tower of RAF Elvington, the Yorkshire Air Museum has rapidly developed an impressive image. The watch tower has been carefully restored to its days when it was a Second World War base for Handley Page Halifaxes and although it looks out on to an apron of aircraft from a different era, is rich in atmosphere. All around wartime buildings have been restored, including the excellent NAAFI. One of the display halls is devoted to the extensive Barnes Wallis collection, including much personal memorabilia and a fascinating display on the Swallow swing-wing experiments. Other displays include aero engines, the air gunners room and the life and times of Robert Blackburn.

Aircraft exhibits:

☐	'G-AAAH'	DH Moth FSM	§ '28
☐	'G-AFFI'	Mignet HM.14 Flying Flea (BAPC.76)	Fr '36
☐	G-AVPN	HP Herald 213	'64
☐	G-YURO	Europa Aviation Europa	'92
☐	'F943'	RAF SE.5A repro (G-BKDT)	'18
☐	'H1968'	Avro 504K repro (BAPC.42)	§ '17
☐	'R6690'	V-S Spitfire FSM (BAPC.254) [PR-A]	'40
☐	HJ711	DH Mosquito NF.II [VI-C]	'43
☐	LV907	HP Halifax II (HR792) [NP-F]	'43
☐	'TJ704'	Beagle Terrier 2 (G-ASCD) [JA]	'48
☐	VV901	Avro Anson T.21	§ '49
☐	WH846	EE Canberra T.4	'54

☐ WH903	EE Canberra B.2 nose	'53
☐ 'WK864'	Gloster Meteor F.8 [C]	'53
☐ WG718	Westland Dragonfly HR.3	§ US '52
☐ WH991	Westland Dragonfly HR.3	§ US '53
☐ WS788	Gloster Meteor NF.14 [Z]	'54
☐ WX788	DH Venom NF.3	§ '54
☐ XL231	HP Victor K.2	'62
☐ XL572	Hawker Hunter T.7 (G-HNTR) [83]	'58
☐ XN974	HS Buccaneer S.2	'64
☐ XP640	Hunting Jet Provost T.4 [D]	'62
☐ XS903	EE Lightning F.6	'66
☐ XX901	HS Buccaneer S.2B	'77
☐ 21417	Lockheed CT-133 Silver Star	US c54
☐ N-268	Hawker Hunter FGA.78	'57
☐ –	RAF BE.2c repro (BAPC.41)	§ '16
☐ –	Blackburn Mercury repro (BAPC.130)	§ '12
☐ –	Hunting Jet Provost T.3 nose	'60
☐ –	Hunting Jet Provost T.3 nose	'60
☐	WACO CG-4A Hadrian fuselage (BAPC.157)	§ '43
☐ –	Messerschmitt Bf 109G FSM (BAPC.240)	Gr '41
☐ –	Port Victoria Grain Kitten repro	§ '16

Nearby:
Castle Howard, *14 miles.*
Eden Camp, *16 miles – see page 100.*
National Railway Museum, *5 miles.*
Real Aeroplane Museum, *12 miles – see page 102.*
City of York, *5 miles.*

ALSO IN YORKSHIRE

Displayed inside the **CORN EXCHANGE** in Leeds is a reproduction Wright Flyer (BAPC.28) of 1903.

The original watch tower now looks out on warplanes of another generation: background Victor K.2, foreground Hunter FGA.78 and Canberra T.4.
Steve Hague

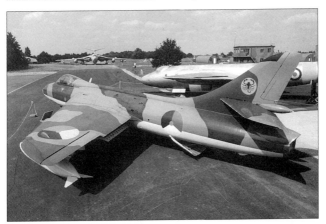

SCOTLAND

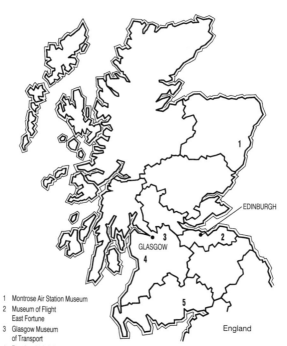

1 Montrose Air Station Museum
2 Museum of Flight
  East Fortune
3 Glasgow Museum
  of Transport
4 Dundonald Aviation
  Visitor Centre
5 Dumfries & Galloway
  Aviation Museum

EDINBURGH

GLASGOW

England

Scottish Tourist Board
23 Ravelston Terrace, Edinburgh, EH4 3EU
Tel: 0131 3322433, Fax: 0131 3431513

DUMFRIES AND GALLOWAY AVIATION MUSEUM
Dumfries

Address: David Reid, Chairman, 11 Ninian Court, Lochside, Dumfries.

Telephone: 01387 251623 (recorded message).

Where: Within the Heathhall Industrial Estate, on the former airfield, off the A701 to the north of the town.

Open: Saturdays and Sundays 10am to 5pm Easter to October. Additionally, Wednesday evenings, 6pm to 9pm July to September. Or by prior arrangement.

By bus: Service to Heathhall from Dumfries.

By rail: Dumfries 3 miles.

Tourist: Dumfries 01387 253862.

Admission: Adult £1.50, Child 75p.

Facilities: Toilets/Parking/Cafe*/Shop/Disabled*/ All*/Changes/Brochure.

Run by the Dumfries and Galloway Aviation Group, the airfield's former watch tower as its centre piece, there is also an aircraft display park. With respect to the airframes, the magic of the museum is to be found within the many intriguing displays inside the watch tower, including life on the RAF station during the Second World War, the 'fruits' of many local aviation archaeology excavations and much more.

Aircraft exhibits:

☐ P7540	V-S Spitfire IIA	§ '41
☐ AD540	V-S Spitfire V wreck	§ '41
☐ WA576	Bristol Sycamore 3	'51
☐ WD386	DHC Chipmunk T.10	§ Can '51
☐ WJ880	EE Canberra T.4 nose	'55
☐ WL375	Gloster Meteor T.7(mod)	'52
☐ XD547	DH Vampire T.11 [Z]	'54
☐ FT-36	Lockheed T-33A 'T-Bird'	US '55
☐ 318	Dassault Mystère IVA [8-NY]	Fr '55
☐ 42163	NA F-100D Super Sabre	US '54
☐ 68-0060	GD F-111E cockpit	US '68

Nearby:
Castle Douglas, *16 miles.*
Dumfries, *3 miles.*

In front of the wartime watch tower at Dumfries, 'tiger' painted Mystère IVA 318. Roger Richards

DUNDONALD AVIATION VISITOR CENTRE
Dundonald, near Troon

Address: The Crossroads, Dundonald,
Strathclyde, KA2 9BT.
Telephone: 01563 850215.
Where: On the B730 north east of Troon.
Open: Daily.
By Bus: Regular services from Irvine and
Kilmarnock.
By Rail: Troon, 7 miles.
Tourist: Troon* 01292 317696,
Kilmarnock 01563 539090.
Admission: All 75p, family ticket £5.00 per year.
Facilities: Toilets/Parking/Cafe*/All/Changes.

A part of Fraser's Garden Centre, the collection –
started by Douglas Fraser and John Hunter – has
expanded considerably in terms of artefacts with a
display building opened in June 1997. As well as
the three cockpit sections there is a large amount
of artefacts relating to the aviation heritage of the
area. Special events and exhibitions are staged.

Aircraft exhibits:

☐	WJ721	EE Canberra TT.18 nose	'53
☐	XT280	HS Buccaneer S.2B nose	'65
☐	XX888	HS Buccaneer S.2B nose	'74
☐	–	V-S Spitfire fsm	§ c40

Nearby:
Museum of Transport and City of Glasgow,
20 miles – see page 109.
Prestwick Airport, *5 miles.*

One of the display rooms at the Montrose museum. Montrose Aerodrome Museum Society

MONTROSE AIR STATION MUSEUM
Montrose

Address: Waldron Road, Montrose, DD10 9BB.
Telephone: 01674 673107.
Where: Waldron Road, off Northesk Road, the A92 to Montrose.
Open: Sundays 12am to 5pm all year. Afternoons during the summer. Other times by arrangement.
By Bus: Services pass close by.
By Rail: Montrose, 2 miles.
Tourist: Montrose* 01674 672000, Arbroath 01241 872609.
Admission: Adults £1, OAP/Child 50p.
Facilities: Toilets/Parking/Cafe*/Shop/All/ Brochure.

Established in the original Royal Flying Corps Watch Office and RAF Station HQ building on the former Broomfield Aerodrome, which can lay claim to being Britain's first operational air station. Three main display rooms contain artefacts, uniforms, photos etc on the aviation heritage of the Montrose area. A static park displays aircraft and vehicles. Next to the museum is the crescent of three former aircraft sheds built in 1913 and believed to be the oldest surviving structures in the UK – possibly the world – to house aircraft. These hangars are now part of the Broomfield Industrial Estate.

Aircraft exhibits:

☐ XD542*	DH Vampire T.11 [28]	'54
☐ XE340	Hawker Sea Hawk FGA.6	'55
☐ XE874	Vampire T.11 [61]	'55
☐ XJ380	Bristol Sycamore HR.14	'56
☐ XJ723	Westland Whirlwind HAR.10	'55

Nearby:
Caledonian Railway Centre, Brechin, 8 miles.
Basin Wildlife centre, 4 miles.

MUSEUM OF TRANSPORT
Glasgow

Address: Kelvin Hall, 1 Bunhouse Road, Glasgow, G3 8DP.
Telephone: 0141 2872623, Fax: 0141 2872692.
Where: To the north west of the city centre, close to the Art Gallery and Museum.
Open: Monday to Saturday 10am to 5pm and Sunday 11am to 5pm.
By bus: Several services available.
By rail: Glasgow Central 2 miles. Kelvin Hall underground.
Tourist: Glasgow 0141 2044400.
Admission: Free.
Facilities: Toilets/Cafe/Shop/Disabled/All/ Changes/Brochure.

A large display of cars, coaches – motorised and horse drawn, locomotives, trams and fire appliances. The pioneering Kay Gyroplane is on loan to the Museum of Flight - see page 110 – for the 1998 season. Additional displays include Scottish made cars, the Clyde room full of impressive ship models, a full-scale railway station platform and a Scottish street reconstruction of around 1938.

Aircraft exhibits:

☐ –	Pilcher Hawk replica (BAPC.48)	§ 1896

Nearby:
City of Glasgow, use the underground network.
Dundonald Aviation Visitor Centre, 20 miles – see page 108.
Greenock, 20 miles.

NATIONAL MUSEUMS OF SCOTLAND – MUSEUM OF FLIGHT
East Fortune Airfield

....

Address: East Fortune Airfield, East Lothian, EH39 5LF.

Telephone: 01620 88308, Fax: 01620 88355.
E-mail: aes@nms.ac.uk
Web-site: http://www.nms.ac.uk

Where: Signed off the A1, off the B1347 near Haddington.

Open: 10.30am to 5pm seven days a week mid-March to mid-November. Weekdays only mid-November to mid-March. Closed 21st December to 4th January. Parties at other times by appointment.

By bus: Service 121 from North Berwick, 6 miles.

By rail: North Berwick, 6 miles..

Tourist: North Berwick 01620 892197.

Admission: Adult £3.00, OAP £1.50, children free.

Facilities: Toilets/Parking/Cafe/Shop/Disabled/Kids/All/Changes/Brochure.

East Fortune airfield was the departure point for the R34 airship on its historic Atlantic crossing of 1919. The entire airfield has been declared an historic monument, including buildings dating back to the First World War. There are over 30 aircraft on display ranging from a Falklands veteran Vulcan to a pair of MiG-15s. There is an exceptional display on air traffic control, a rocketry exhibition, a wide selection of aero engines and a space gallery. A continual, and fascinating, theme throughout the museum is the nature of flight and how man flies. Special exhibitions and occasion special events are held. A flying display, the 'Festival of Flight' was first staged in 1997 and looks set to become an annual event. The museum has a policy of running daily tours to the third (storage) hangar where visitors can see items not on permanent display plus restoration projects (including a Spitfire F.21 for eventual display in Glasgow).

Aircraft exhibits:

☐ G-ACVA	Kay Gyroplane	'34
☐ G-ACYK	Spartan Cruiser III fuselage	'34
☐ G-AFJU	Miles Monarch	§ '38
☐ G-AGBN	GAL Cygnet II	'40
☐ G-AHKY	Miles M.18-2	'39

Spartan Cruiser G-ACYK which crashed in Scotland in January 1938. Only the centre fuselage and cockpit remains of this unique reminder of a 1930s airliner. Ken Ellis collection

☐ G-ANOV	DH Dove 6	'54
☐ G-AOEL	DH Tiger Moth	'40
☐ G-ARCX	Gloster Meteor Mk 14	'52
☐ G-ASUG	Beech D.18S	US '56
☐ G-ATFG	Brantly B.2B	US '65
☐ G-ATOY	Piper Comanche 260B fuselage	US '65
☐ G-AXEH	SAL Bulldog Srs 1	'69
☐ G-BBVF	SAL Twin Pioneer 2	'58
☐ G-BDFU	Dragonfly man-powered aircraft	§ '75
☐ G-BDIX	DH Comet 4C	'62
☐ G-JSSD	HP Jetstream 3100	'69
☐ VH-SNB	DH Dragon I	'34
☐ VH-UQB	DH Puss Moth	§ '34
☐ W-2	Weir W-2 autogyro (BAPC.85)	'34
☐ LA198	V-S Spitfire F.21 [RAI-G]	§ '45
☐ TE462	V-S Spitfire XVI	'45
☐ 'TJ398'	Auster AOP.6 (BAPC.70)	§ '44
☐ TS291	Slingsby Tutor glider (BCB)	'45
☐ VM360	Avro Anson C.19 (G-APHV)	§ '47
☐ VX185	EE Canberra B.8 nose	'51
☐ WF259	Hawker Sea Hawk F.2 [171-A]	'54
☐ WV493	Percival Provost T.1 (G-BDYG) [29]	'53
☐ WW145	DH Sea Venom FAW.22 [680-LM]	'55
☐ XA109	DH Sea Vampire T.22	§ '54
☐ XG594	Westland Whirlwind HAS.7 [517-PO]	US '57
☐ XL762	SARO Skeeter AOP.12	'58
☐ XM597	Avro Vulcan B.2	'63

☐ XN776	EE Lightning F.2A [C]	'62
☐ XT288	HS Buccaneer S.2B	'66
☐ 309	MiG-15UTI 'Midget'	Ru c55
☐ 591	Schleicher Rhonlerche II	Gr c60
☐ 3677	MiG MiG-15bis 'Fagot'	Ru c53
☐ 9940	Bristol Bolingbroke IVT	'44
☐ 191659	Messerschmitt Me 163B-1a [15]	Gr '45
☐ –	Albatros ASG.21 hang-glider	
	(BAPC.247)	Ger '77
☐ –	Chargus 18/50 hang glider (BAPC.160)	c75
☐ –	Cirrus 3 hang glider (BAPC.197)	c75
☐ –	Electra Floater hang-glider	
	(BAPC.245)	US '79
☐ –	Hiway Cloudbase hang-glider	
	(BAPC.246)	'78
☐ –	HP Jetstream 1 (N14234) fuselage	'69
☐ –	Moonraker 77 hang glider (BAPC.195)	c77
☐ –	MS.505 Criquet (G-BIRW) [FI+S]	Gr '47
☐ –	Pilcher Hawk (BAPC.49)	1896
☐ –	Sigma IIM hang glider (BAPC.196)	c80
☐ –	Slingsby Gull I glider (BED)	c46
☐ –	Slingsby T.21B glider (BJV)	c60
☐ –	Solo Typhoon hang-glider (BAPC.244)	'81
☐ –	WACO CG-4A Hadrian nose	US '44

Nearby:
City of Edinburgh, *20 miles.*
Myreton Motor Museum, *5 miles.*

Miles M.18 U8 (now G-AHKY) built in 1939 with the aim of replacing the Magister. Ken Ellis collection

Above: **The prototype Bulldog, at the Museum of Flight. Built by Beagle at Shoreham, Sussex in 1969, the type went into production at Prestwick with Scottish Aviation.** Alan Curry

Below: **Lightning F.2A XN776, also at the Museum of Flight. This is the only one of its variant preserved intact in the UK.** Alan Curry

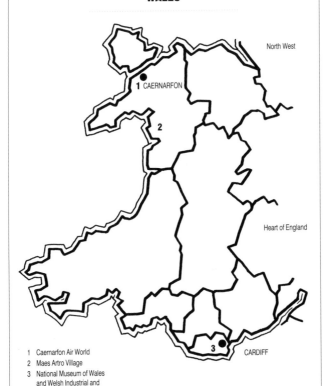

WALES

North West

1 CAERNARFON

2

Heart of England

3 CARDIFF

1 Caernarfon Air World
2 Maes Artro Village
3 National Museum of Wales
  and Welsh Industrial and
  Maritime Museum

Wales Tourist Board
Brunel House, 2 Fitzalan Road, Cardiff, CF2 1UY
Tel: 01222 499909 Fax: 01222 485031

CAERNARFON AIR WORLD
Caernarfon Aerodrome, Gwynedd

Address: Air Caernarfon Ltd, Caernarfon Airport,
Llandwrog, Caernarfon, Gwynedd, LL54 5TP.
Telephone: 01286 830800, Fax: 01286 830280.
Where: At Caernarfon aerodrome, north of the
A487 and signposted from Llandwrog.
Open: March to November, 9am to 5.30pm.
Groups at other times can be arranged.
By bus: Services pass close by, enquiries via
museum.
By rail: Bangor 12 miles.
Tourist: Caernarfon 01267 231557.
Admission: Adult £4.00, Child £2.50.
Facilities: Toilets/Parking/Cafe/Shop/Disabled/
Kids/All/Changes/Brochure.

Situated within sight of the Snowdon mountain range, the museum naturally includes themes relating to mountain rescue and to mountain crashes. The history of RAF Llandwrog is well illustrated. Visitors can see the restoration of the Anson underway at weekends. Pleasure flying is run during the summer season from the aerodrome, often using DH Dragon Rapide G-AIDL. Views of the activity on the aerodrome can be seen to advantage from the museum.

Aircraft exhibits:

☐ G-ALFT	DH Dove 6	'49
☐ G-AMLZ	Percival Prince 6E	'51
☐ G-AWUK	Cessna F.150H cockpit	US
☐ G-MBEP	American Aerolights Eagle 215B	US '81
☐ TX235	Avro Anson C.19/2	'46
☐ WM961	Hawker Sea Hawk FB.5 [J]	'54
☐ WN499	Westland Dragonfly HR.3 [Y]	US '53
☐ WV781	Bristol Sycamore HR.12	'52
☐ WT694	Hawker Hunter F.1	'54
☐ XA282	Slingsby Cadet TX.3	'52
☐ XH837	Gloster Javelin FAW.7 nose	'58
☐ XJ726	Westland Whirlwind HAR.10 [F]	US '55
☐ XK623	DH Vampire T.11 [56]	'56
☐ XL618	Hawker Hunter T.7 [05]	'59
☐ –	Mignet HM.14 Flying Flea (BAPC 201)	Fr '36
☐ –	Weedhopper JC-24	US c78

Nearby:
Bangor and the Menai Bridge, *12 miles.*
Caernarfon, *4 miles.*
Ffestiniog Railway, *16 miles.*
Llanberis Lake Railway, *8 miles.*
Portmeirion Village, *16 miles.*
Snowdon Mountain Railway, *10 miles.*

See also illustration on page 117.

Clever use of mural and the salvaged 'tail feathers' of an Anson to show a high ground incident. Ken Ellis

MAES ARTRO VILLAGE
Llanbedr, Gwynedd

Address: Artro Enterprises, Reception Building, Maes Artro, Llanbedr, Gwynedd, LL45 2PZ.

Telephone: 01341 241467.

Where: In Llanbedr village, south of Harlech on the A496.

Open: Daily Easter to the end of September 10am to 5.30pm.

By bus: Services to Barmouth and Harlech pass close to the entrance.

By rail: Llanbedr Halt on the Cambrian Coast line, half mile.

Tourist: Barmouth* 01654 761244.

Admission: Adult £3.00, OAP £2.50, Child £2.50.

Facilities: Toilets/Parking/Cafe/Shop/Disabled/ Kids/All/Brochure.

Part of the former domestic site for the nearby air-field has been turned into an attractive visitor centre appealing to everyone. From an aviation viewpoint, the history of Llanbedr airfield and its surroundings are well covered and work on the restoration of the Anson – a long time resident at the airfield – is possible during weekends. Also included on the site is a recreated old Welsh-style street, rural heritage exhibition, sea life aquarium, woodland walk and much, much more.

Aircraft exhibits:

☐ 'MAV467'	V-S Spitfire V FSM (BAPC.202)	'45
☐ VS562	Avro Anson T.21	'48
☐ XJ409	Westland Whirlwind HAR.10	US '53
☐ –	Hawker Hunter cockpit	c55
☐ A92-664	GAF Jindivik 4A drone	Aus c57

Nearby:
Fairbourne Railway, *8 miles*.

Ffestiniog Railway, *10 miles*.

Portmeirion Village, *10 miles*.

Shell Island – offering good views of activity at the Test & Experimental Establishment Llanbedr, *2 miles*.

Above: **Serving for many years from the nearby airfield have been Jindivik drones. A92-664 is displayed at Maes Artro.** Nigel Price

Below: **The Maes Artro Anson in its original guise as the prototype T.21.** Author's collection

NATIONAL MUSEUM OF WALES
Cardiff

Address: Cathays Park, Museum Avenue, Cardiff, CF1 3NP
Telephone: 01222 397951, Fax: 01222 373219.
Where: North of the city centre, close to Cathays Station and Cardiff Castle. Signposted.
Open: Tuesday to Sunday, plus Bank Holidays 10am to 5pm.
By Bus: Services pass close by.
By Rail: Cathays Station, adjacent.
Tourist: Cardiff, 01222 499909, Fax: 01222 485031.
Admission: Adult £4.25, OAP/child £2.50, family ticket £9.75.
Facilities: Toilets/Parking/Cafe/Shop/Disabled/All/Changes/Brochure.

As part of the museum's 70th anniversary celebrations, during early January 1998 the Watkins CHW Monoplane was installed, after many years in storage at nearby RAF St Athan. Built by C H Watkins at friends at Maendy, Cardiff, from 1907, the monoplane – powered by a three cylinder engine designed by Watkins – is claimed to have made its

first flight in 1909 and was performing cross-countries by 1910. It was retired in 1916. Whatever the dates of its first flight and their nature, it is the oldest aircraft of Welsh origin. The museum has many remarkable collections, including botany, zoology and geology plus a wide range of paintings and other works of art.

Aircraft exhibit:

☐ – Watkins CHW Monoplane (BAPC.47) '09

Nearby:
Cardiff City centre, walking distance.
Welsh Industrial and Maritime Museum, *2 miles*

Note:

The **WALES AIRCRAFT MUSEUM** at Cardiff – Wales Airport closed in early 1996. The **WELSH INDUSTRIAL AND MARITIME MUSEUM** closed on 31st May 1998 and their only aviation exhibit, Westland Wessex HAS.1 XM300, was put up for disposal.

Newly on display at the National Museum of Wales is the oldest aircraft of Welsh origin, the Watkins CHW Monoplane, which dates from 1907. Author's collection

ALSO IN WALES

At Swansea Airport, **DE HAVILLAND AVIATION** stage regular open days of their classic jet aircraft, both operational and under restoration. Included are DH Vampire T.11s WZ507 (G-VTII) and XE920 (G-VMPR), T.55 U-1234 (G-DHAV), FB.6 'WL505' (G-MKVI), Sea Vixen D.3 XP924 (G-CVIX) and Sea Devon C.20 XK895 (G-SDEV). During open days, depending on operational circumstances aircraft are ground-run, or even flown. More details on 01656 729057.

De Havilland Aviation at Swansea Airport hold regular open days when their collection of classic jets can be viewed. Ken Ellis

The Air Caernarfon/Air Atlantique Dragon Rapide occasionally operates around Snowdonia but is also to be found earning its keep at Coventry and air shows nationwide. Ken Ellis

NORTHERN IRELAND

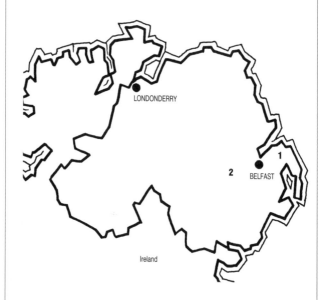

LONDONDERRY

2

BELFAST

1

Ireland

1 Ulster Folk and
  Transport Museum
2 Ulster Aviation Museum

Northern Ireland Tourist Board
St Anne's Court, 59 North Street, Belfast, BT1 1NB
Tel: 01232 231221 Fax: 01232 240960

ULSTER AVIATION MUSEUM

Langford Lodge

Address: 33 Old Mill Meadows, Dundonald,
BT16 0WQ.
Telephone: 01849 454444.
Where: At Langford Lodge Aerodrome, on the
shores of Lough Neagh, west of Belfast.
Open: Open Saturdays 1pm to 5pm and at other
times by prior appointment.
Tourist: Belfast International Airport 01849
422888, Fax: 01849 452084.
Admission: TBA.
Facilities: Toilets/Parking/All/Changes.

Established by the Ulster Aviation Society, who
have been collecting airframes and artefacts to tell
the story of aviation in Northern Ireland for many
years, the centre is set in former US Second War

buildings at Langford Lodge. Displays and facilities are expanding all the time and the control
tower is being refurbished as both an exhibit and
extension to the display space.

Aircraft exhibits:

☐ G-BDBS	Shorts 330	'75
☐ EI-BUO	Lavery Sea Hawker homebuilt	US '88
☐ JV482	Grumman Wildcat V	US '
☐ WN108	Hawker Sea Hawk FB.3 [033]	'54
☐ WZ549	DH Vampire T.11 [F]	'53
☐ XV361	HS Buccaneer S.2	'68
☐ –	hang-glider	?

Nearby:
City of Belfast, *9 miles*.
Ulster Folk and Transport Museum, *20 miles –
see page 120*.

See also page 121

Visitors to the Ulster Aviation Museum can monitor progress on the restoration of Wildcat V JV482. Ken Ellis

ULSTER FOLK AND TRANSPORT MUSEUM

Holywood, County Down

Address: Cultra, Holywood, Northern Ireland, BT18 0EU.

Telephone: 01232 428428, Fax: 02132 428728.

Where: On the A2 north east of Belfast city centre at Holywood. Well signed.

Open: Open daily all year round, closed three days at Xmas. July-August Monday to Saturday 10.30am to 6pm, Sunday 12am to 6pm; April-June and September Monday-Friday 9.30am to 5pm, Saturday 10.30am to 6pm, Sunday 12am to 6pm; October to March Monday to Friday 9.30am to 4pm and Saturday-Sunday 12.30am to 4.30pm.

By bus: Services from Belfast to Holywood and beyond past the entrance.

By rail: Cultra, 200 yards.

Tourist: 01232 231221, Fax: 01232 240960.

Admission: Adult £3.30, OAP/Child £2.20, Family ticket £8.

Facilities: Toilets/Parking/Cafe/Shop/Disabled/ All/Changes/Brochure.

The transport element of this extensive museum has prospered in recent years with the opening in 1993 of an amazing railway hall and a land transport hall in 1995. It is hoped that more space can then be devoted to aviation as the Province has a rich heritage to show off. Currently the 'original' Ferguson replica and the Short SC.1 are used to show the full sweep of aviation development. In a superb display devoted to the life and works of Rex McCandless, two of his autogyros are displayed as well as his legendary motorcycles and the four-wheel drive 'buggy'. Across the road on the 'Folk' site can be found an incredible village of buildings moved and reconstructed, brick-by-brick from sites all over Northern Ireland. Regular special displays and exhibitions and other attractions, details on application.

Aircraft exhibits:

☐	G-AJOC	Miles Messenger 2A	§ '47
☐	G-AKEL	Miles Gemini 1A	§ '47
☐	G-AKGE	Miles Gemini 3C	§ '47
☐	G-AKLW	Short Sealand	§ '51
☐	G-AOUR	DH Tiger Moth	§ '44
☐	G-ARTZ	McCandless M-2 gyroplane	'65
☐	G-ATXX	McCandless M-4 gyroplane	'66
☐	VH-UUP	Short Scion I	§ '34
☐	XG905	Short SC.1	'58
☐	–	Ferguson Monoplane replica (IAHC.6)	'09
☐	–	Ferguson Monoplane replica (IAHC.9) § '09
☐	–	Short Nimbus I glider (ALA)	§ '47

Nearby:

City of Belfast, *7 miles*.
North Down Heritage Centre, Bangor, *12 miles*.
Ulster Aviation Museum, *20 miles* – see page 119.

Two Short SC.1 VTOL experimental aircraft were built, the example at Holywood being the second. Shorts

Above: **Within the Ulster Folk and Transport Museum can be found a faithful reproduction of the monoplane built by Ulsterman Harry Ferguson** – he later gained considerable fame for his tractors and ploughing system.

Below: **Largest exhibit with the Ulster Aviation Museum (see page 119) is the second prototype Shorts 330 commuter liner, first flown at Belfast on 8th July 1975.** Both Ken Ellis

IRELAND

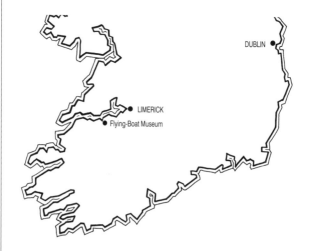

Northern Ireland

DUBLIN ●

● LIMERICK
● Flying-Boat Museum

Irish Tourist Board
150 New Bond Street, London, W1Y 0AQ
Tel: 0171 493 3201 Fax: 0171 493 9065

FLYING-BOAT MUSEUM

Foynes, Limerick

Address: Flying-Boat Museum, Foynes, Limerick.
Telephone: 00 353 69 65416 (also Fax).
Where: On the N69 west of Limerick, well signed.
Open: Open late March to late October, 10am to 6pm.
By bus: Daily service from Limerick.
By rail: Limerick 23 miles.
Admission: Adult £3, Child £1.50, Family £8.
Facilities: Toilets/Parking/Cafe/Shop/Disabled/ All/Brochure.

From 1939 to 1945 Foynes was famous as the only place from which non-stop services to and from the USA could be made. The museum is centred around the original terminal building, control tower, radio and weather rooms of the famous flying-boat station. The museum records the magnificent era of the flying-boat and Ireland's vital role to the Allied war effort during the Second World War. Foynes was where Irish Coffee was invented and visitors can sample this and other Irish welcomes!

Shades of the Flying-Boat Museum.

Top: **Monument and fountain in the shape of a Boeing 314.**

Bottom: *The Yankee Clipper*, **source of Irish Coffee!**
Both Geoff Simmons

WRECKS & RELICS
16th Edition

Ken Ellis

Wrecks & Relics is an institution. Each edition is eagerly awaited by enthusiasts, historians, owners and operators of historic aircraft and curators of aviation collections as the most trusted and hard-working of references. Now in its 37th year of publication, the 16th edition marks the author's 25th year at the helm and to celebrate, takes an occasional look back at the scene in 1974.

The book takes the reader on a geographical journey through the fascinating world of museums, military stores and dumps, 'geriatric' airliners awaiting the axe, restoration workshops, technical schools, treasures in garages and barns and much more. Fully revised and updated, the 16th edition has an array of appendices and the usual extensive indexing and cross-referencing. The comprehensive photographic section is full of out-of-the-way subjects.

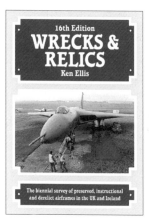

Previous editions still in print:

12th edition (1990) 252pp	**£9.95**	
14th edition (1994) 336pp	**£12.95**	
15th edition (1996) 350pp	**£14.95**	

Hardback
210 x 148 mm, 352 pages
191 b/w photographs
1 85780 079 6
£14.95

EUROPEAN WRECKS & RELICS
2nd Edition

Otger van der Kooij

When the first edition was published in 1989 it was eagerly snapped up by enthusiasts. Now, with inputs from a huge network of sources, the second edition takes the story of Europe's amazing variety of museum, retired and derelict aircraft into the 1990s.

As with the previous edition, and its UK-based partner, *Wrecks & Relics,* this book does not just chronicle what is currently to be found, but all known activity since the first edition appeared. With the astonishing developments in Europe that saw the dissolving of the so-called 'Iron Curtain', *European Wrecks & Relics* charts the 'peace dividend' with details of the disposal of hundreds of military aircraft across the Continent.

Coverage has been extended in this issue to include the Czech Republic, Hungary, Poland and Slovakia. Photographic content is lavish and in full colour.

As with the first edition, this will be a much sought after work being both a faithful touring companion and a much-used reference work to the bygone aircraft of Europe's museums and air forces.

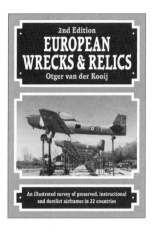

Hardback
210 x 148 mm, 480 pages
About 200 colour photographs
1 85780 085 0   August 1998
c£24.95

Both available from:
Midland Counties Publications
Unit 3 Maizefield, Hinckley Fields,
Hinckley, Leics, LE10 1YF, UK
Tel: 01455 233 747 Fax: 01455 841 805
E-mail: midlandbooks@compuserve.com

Ground crew administering to the needs of the starboard inner of B-17G *Mary Alice* inside the American Air Museum at the Imperial War Museum, Duxford – see page 10. Ken Ellis

INDEX

As well as listing county names, this index has been extended to list some museums also by 'alternative' or 'generic' names to aid reference.

We hope that you have enjoyed this Midland Publishing book. Our titles are carefully produced for you by a knowledgeable and enthusiastic team of specialists. Further titles are in the course of preparation but we would welcome ideas on what you would like to see. If you have a manuscript or project that requires publishing, we should be happy to consider it; brief details initially, please.

In addition, our associate company, Midland Counties Publications, offer an exceptionally wide range of aviation and railway books/videos for sale by mail-order around the world. For a copy of the appropriate catalogue, please write, telephone, fax or e-mail:

Midland Counties Publications,
Unit 3 Maizefield, Hinckley Fields, Hinckley, Leics, LE10 1YF.
Tel: 01455 233 747; Fax: 01455 841 805.
E-mail: midlandbooks@compuserve.com